Cha. O. Brown

M. SKYTTE CHRISTIANSEN

THE POCKET
ENCYCLOPAEDIA OF
WILD FLOWERS
IN COLOUR

667 illustrations by
HENNING ANTHON

Translated and Edited by
VERA HIGGINS

BLANDFORD PRESS
LONDON

First published in the English edition
© 1965 by Blandford Press Ltd.,
167 High Holborn, London WC IV 6 PH
Second impression 1967
Third impression 1971
Fourth impression 1974
ISBN 0 7137 0374 1

Originally published in Denmark as
Flora i Farver
by Politikens Forlag 1962

Printed in Holland by The Ysel Press Ltd., Deventer
and bound in Great Britain.

EDITOR'S PREFACE

The British love of flowers is well known and is exemplified in their gardens, but many people who travel about the country are interested in some of the wild flowers they find, and would like to know the names. Identification by means of coloured illustration is not difficult, and this book should be useful.

It is an interesting fact, that although the book was first published in Denmark, of the 667 plants illustrated, all but 39 of them are native to the British Isles. These 39 plants, however, are often cultivated in our woods or gardens and would be familiar.

As well as English names, the Latin or so-called botanical names are given; these are the same in all countries throughout the world. Not all the plants of this country have genuine English names, that is, names given by local residents—villagers, farmers, and people who meet them in their daily lives—the English names are now being invented where they do not exist; it is common practice to put invented names in inverted commas to distinguish them from genuine common names. I would strongly recommend people who are interested in identifying wild plants to become accustomed to the Latin names; to quote a well known example, the name Bluebell is used in England and Scotland for quite different plants; the English Bluebell is also known as the Wild Hyacinth. On the other hand, the Bluebell of Scotland is *Campanula rotundifolia,* and in the south is called the Harebell, which shows the value of using a Latin name for identification purposes.   V.H.

FOREWORD

This book contains pictures of 667 plant species and is designed to assist all those who would like to become acquainted with wild flowering plants.

No specific previous knowledge of botany is needed in order to use this book. The name of the unknown plant will be found by comparing the plant with the pictures in the colour plates, and the final 'determination' of the plant can be checked by reading the corresponding description at the end of the book.

The book begins with lists stating what plant species one may expect to find in the different types of locality. In these lists the plants have been arranged according to the colour of their flowers, which should make it comparatively easy to find the species of the plant in question.

For obvious reasons, grasses and grasslike plants are represented comparatively sparsely; but apart from these large and difficult groups of plants there are pictures or descriptions of all fairly common, wild flowering plants.

It is our hope that this little book will help to awaken a sense of appreciation of the irreplaceable value of the beauty of wild flora, and in this way contribute to the protection of the wild plant sanctuaries.

Copenhagen, June, 1962

HENNING ANTHON   M. SKYTTE CHRISTIANSEN

CONTENTS

PLANT LOCALITIES

Each individual plant species makes its own very special demands on its environment and cannot hold its own in competition with other plant species unless these demands are complied with. Thus, some plants can only grow in the shade of the forest where it is cool and damp, others demand warm, light, open soil; others again occur exclusively on permanently moist soil or in the water itself; some demand clayey, rich soil; others may thrive on poor, sandy ground, et cetera.

Plants needing approximately similar conditions will be able to grow together, forming so-called *plant communities*. Each of these communities occurs in a definite locality, where the conditions more or less have put a common stamp on the members of the plant community.

On the following pages there are lists stating which of the plants illustrated one may expect to find in the different localities. These lists of plants are intended to help in finding the name of an unknown plant. One simply looks up likely plants and will finally find the right one.

In order to simplify this task, plants growing in different localities have been arranged according to the colour of their flowers, while grasses and grass-like plants have been listed at the end.

Trees and bushes are *not* included in the plant lists, although they have, of course, been included in the colour plates.

GROUPING OF PLANT LOCALITIES

Plant localities have been placed in the following groups:

In each 'plant community' the composition of the vegetation varies according to the humidity of the soil and its plant food content, and consequently one cannot expect to find in one and the same place all the plant species given in the same list. On the other hand, one will find several plant species listed in more than one group.

On *the shore*, the surge of the waves has a strong influence. Consequently, other plants will be found along sandy or stony coasts than on clayey shores or on heaps of rotten, washed-up seaweed. In maritime meadows one can also observe that the different plant species are distributed in zones from the shore inland, according to their ability to tolerate salt in the subsoil water.

Nor do soil conditions alone determine the ground vegetation in *the wood;* the trees, rulers of the forest, contribute to an equally large extent. Only plants which tolerate deep shade all through the summer will thrive in the dense beech woods. On the other hand, plants needing more light will thrive in the light shade of oak and ash, etc. Plants needing even more light will be found in forest clearings. The forest 'litter', the fallen leaves, are also needed for the development of forest-floor plants. Where the soil has the right degree of humidity, the dead leaves are decomposed by earthworms and other creatures in the forest and later transformed into leaf-mould, rendering part of the food which the tree-roots have brought up from the soil accessible to the plants of the forest once more. Where the soil is too dry for earthworms to live, on the other hand, the forest litter remains lying on the surface and becomes shot through with roots and fungus threads, forming a firm, peat-like layer which is called raw humus. The raw humus soil is poor in easily accessible plant food and harbours a forest-floor flora which is different from that thriving in leaf-mould soil.

On *cultivated soil,* the kind of crop grown on it plays an important part for the composition of the weed flora in addition to the soil conditions. Thus, in grass and clover fields the weed species differ from those in cornfields and among root-crops. Other species again occur chiefly in well-fertilized soil in gardens or on rubbish-heaps and on roadsides around towns and buildings.

GROUP I

Plants in and on the shores of lakes, ponds and streams

a. Plants with White Flowers

8. *Calla palustris*	258. Awlwort	473. Bogbean
14. Arrow-head	292. Meadow-sweet	476. Bellbine, Larger Bindweed
23. Canadian Pondweed	415. Cowbane	
24. Frog-bit	425. Hog's Fennel	513. 'Gipsy-wort'
25. Water Soldier	426. Water Parsnip	565. 'Marsh Bedstraw'
163. Marsh Stitchwort	427. Narrow-leaved Water Parsnip	565a. 'Swamp Bedstraw'
194. White Water-lily		578. 'Elder-leaved Valerian'
213. 'Water Crowfoot'	429. 'Fine-leaved Water Dropwort'	
241. Watercress		

b. Plants with Yellow Flowers

39. Yellow Flag	223. Celery-leaved Crowfoot	462. 'Tufted Loosestrife'
195. Yellow Water-lily		553. 'Greater Bladderwort'
202. Kingcup, Marsh Marigold	242. 'Great Yellow-cress'	
	243. 'Marsh Yellow-cress'	608. 'Nodding Bur-Marigold'
216. Greater Spearwort	303. Silverweed	
219. Lesser Spearwort	460. 'Yellow Loosestrife'	609. 'Tripartite Bur-Marigold'

c. Plants with Red, Pink or Reddish-Purple Flowers

15. Water Plantain
16. Flowering Rush
151. 'Amphibious Bistort'
309. 'Marsh Cinquefoil'
397. Purple Loosestrife

400. Great Hairy Willow-herb
402. 'Marsh Willow-herb'
428. Water Dropwort
459. Water Violet

473. Bogbean
509. Marsh Woundwort
537. 'Marsh Speedwell'
578. 'Elder-leaved Valerian'
591. Hemp Agrimony

d. Plants with Blue, Pale Blue or Bluish-Purple Flowers

482. Water Forget-me-not
482a. Water Forget-me-not
495. Skull-cap

514. 'Corn Mint'
515. 'Water Mint'
517. Woody Nightshade

535. Brooklime
535a. Water Speedwell
637. 'Marsh Speedwell'
590. 'Water Lobelia'

e. Plants with Greenish or Brownish Flowers

5. 'Great Reedmace'
5a. 'Lesser Reedmace'
6. Bur-reed
7. 'Unbranched Bur-reed'
10. Sweet Flag
11. 'Ivy Duckweed'

12. Duckweed
13. 'Great Duckweed'
138. Stinging Nettle
196. Hornwort
365. 'Stagnant Water Starwort'

393. 'Spiked Water-milfoil'
394. Mare's tail
409. Pennywort
560. Shore-weed
602. 'Marsh Cudweed'

f. Grasses and Grass-like Plants

40. 'Jointed Rush'
41. 'Compact Rush'
42. Soft Rush
43. Toad Rush
49. Reed
52. Flote-grass

53. Reed-grass
54. Reed-grass
74a. Common Bent Grass, Fine Bent, Purple Bent
77. 'Marsh Foxtail'

87. Bulrush
88. 'Sea Club-Rush'
90. 'Common Spikerush'
93. 'Common Sedge'
94. 'Tufted Sedge'
100. 'Beaked Sedge'

GROUP II

Plants from bogs and meadows

a. Plants with White Flowers

163. 'Marsh Stitchwort'
164. 'Lesser Stitchwort'
169. 'Common Mouse-ear Chickweed'
173. 'Knotted Pearlwort'
241. Watercress
245. 'Large Bitter-cress'
257. Whitlow Grass
279. Grass of Parnassus

292. Meadow-sweet
333. White Clover, Dutch Clover
363. Common Milkwort
364. 'Purging Flax'
384. Sundew
411. 'Rough Chervil'
416. Caraway
420. Wild Angelica

422a. Cow-parsnip, Hog-weed
425. Hog's Fennel
434. Larger Wintergreen
448. Bog Whortleberry
473. Buckbean, Bogbean
476. Bellbine, Larger Bindweed
539. Eyebright

563. 'Northern Bedstraw'
565. 'Marsh Bedstraw'
565a. 'Swamp Bedstraw'
566. 'Hedge Greater Bed-straw'
577. Marsh Valerian
578. 'Elder-leaved Vale-rian'
597. Daisy
613. Sneezewort
614. Yarrow
616. Marguerite, Moon-Daisy, Ox-eye Daisy

b. Plants with Yellow Flowers

34. Bog Asphodel
198. 'Common Meadow Rue'
202. Kingcup, Marsh Marigold
203. 'Globe Flower'
217. Goldilocks
218. Meadow Buttercup
219. Lesser Spearwort
220. Lesser Celandine
221. 'Creeping Buttercup'
223. 'Celery-leaved Crow-foot'
238. Winter Cress, Yellow Rocket

302. 'Creeping Cinque-foil'
303. Silverweed
305. Common Tormentil
326. 'Lesser Yellow Tre-foil'
339. Birdsfoot Trefoil
340. Large Birdsfoot Tre-foil
344. 'Meadow Vetchling'
380. 'Imperforate St John's Wort'
458. Cowslip, Paigle
460. 'Yellow Loosestrife'

461. Creeping Jenny
462. 'Tufted Loosestrife'
544. Greater Yellowrattle
545. Yellow-rattle
607. 'Willow-leaved Inula'
643. 'Cabbage Thistle'
655. 'Autumnal Hawkbit'
656. Goat's-beard, Jack-go-to-bed-at-noon
660. Common Dandelion
662. 'Bitten-off Hawk's-beard
664. Marsh Hawk's-beard

c. Plants with Red, Pink or Reddish-Purple Flowers

103. Fragrant Orchid
107. Meadow Orchis
107a. Marsh Orchis
108. Spotted Orchis
111. 'Marsh Helleborine'
144. Sorrel
185. Ragged Robin
186. Red Campion
244. Cuckoo Flower, Lady's Smock
295. Water Avens
309. 'Marsh Cinquefoil'
330. Red Clover
363. Common Milkwort

397. Purple Loosestrife
400. Great Hairy Willow-herb
402. 'Marsh Willow-herb'
416. Caraway
420. Wild Angelica
443. Marsh Andromeda
446. Cranberry
448. 'Bog Whortleberry'
450. Ling, Heather
451. Cross-leaved Heath, Bog Heather
457. 'Bird's-eye Primrose'
473. Bogbean

487. Comfrey
509. Marsh Woundwort
537. Marsh Speedwell
538. Red Bartsia
547. Red-rattle
548. Lousewort
577. Marsh Valerian
578. 'Elder-leaved Vale-rian'
591. Hemp Agrimony
626. Butterbur
640. Marsh Thistle
645. Saw-wort
648. Brown-rayed Knap-wort

d. Plants with Blue, Pale Blue or Bluish-Purple Flowers

244. Lady's Smock
349. Tufted Vetch
363. Common Milkwort
389. 'Marsh Violet'
469. Marsh Gentian

482. 'Water Forget-me-not'
482a.'Water Forget-me-not'
487. Comfrey

493. Bugle
495. Skull-cap
496. Self-heal
504. Ground Ivy
515. 'Water Mint'

517. Woody Nightshade	534. 'Thyme-leaved	539. Eyebright
533. 'Germander Speed-	Speedwell'	554. Common Butterwort
well'	535. Brooklime	579. Devil's-bit Scabious
	537. 'Marsh Speedwell'	588. Harebell, Bluebell

e. Plants with Greenish or Brownish Flowers

112. Coral-root	174. 'Procumbent Pearl-	542. 'Forest Glade Cow-
114. Sorrel	wort'	wheat'
150. Water-pepper	409. Pennywort	555. 'Great Plantain'
	421. 'Seashore Angelica'	557. Ribwort

f. Grasses and Grass-like Plants

17. 'Marsh Arrow-grass'	58a. Rough Meadow-	78. Timothy
19. 'Marsh Scheuchzeria'	grass	80. 'Sweet Vernal Grass'
40. 'Jointed Rush'	61. Cock's-foot	81. Rye Grass
41. 'Compact Rush'	62. Quaking Grass,	83. Holy Grass
42. Soft Rush	Doddering Dillies	85. 'Hare's-tail'
43. Toad Rush	63. 'Crested Dog's-tail'	85. 'Common Cotton
45. Sweep's Brush	64. 'Hairy Oat'	Grass'
47. 'Purple Moor-grass'	65. 'False Oat-grass'	89. 'Wood Club-rush'
48. Mat-grass	66. 'Tufted Hair Grass'	90. 'Common Spikerush'
49. Reed	68. Yorkshire Fog	91. 'White Beak-Sedge'
55. 'Meadow Fescue'	69. Lop-grass	93. 'Common Sedge'
56. Red Fescue	73. 'Purple Small-reed'	94. 'Tufted Sedge'
58. Meadow-grass	74a. 'Creeping Bent'	95. Carnation Grass
	76. 'Meadow Foxtail'	96. 'White Sedge'
	77. 'Marsh Foxtail'	100. 'Beaked Sedge'

GROUP III

Seashore Plants

a. Seashore Plants with White Flowers

165. Chickweed	333. White Clover, Dutch	497. 'Common Hemp-
169. 'Common Mouse-ear	Clover	nettle'
Chickweed'	335. 'Strawberry Clover'	568. Goosegrass, Cleavers
172. 'Sea Sandwort'	411. 'Rough Chervil'	597. Daisy
176. Sea Sand-Spurrey	476. Bellbine,	614. Yarrow
239. Seakale	Larger Bindweed	618. 'Scentless Mayweed'
260. Scurvy-grass		

b. Seashore Plants with Yellow Flowers

200. 'Lesser Meadow Rue'	223. 'Celery-leaved Crow-	302. 'Creeping Cinquefoil'
218. Meadow Buttercup	foot'	303. Silverweed
222. 'Bulbous Buttercup'	269. Wall-pepper	339. Birdsfoot Trefoil

518. Henbane
525. Toadflax
567. Lady's Bedstraw
607a. 'British Inula'
617. Tansy

621. 'Field Southern-wood'
630. 'Stinking Groundsel'
631. Groundsel

655. 'Autumnal Hawkbit'
658. 'Field Milk-thistle'
660. Common Dandelion
666. Hawkweed

c. Seashore Plants with Red, Pink or Reddish-Purple Flowers

29a. 'Crow Garlic'
148. Knotgrass
176. 'Sea Sand-Spurrey'
176a. 'Winged-seed Sand-spurrey'
335. 'Strawberry Clover'
346. 'Sea Pea'

358. Herb Robert
362. Common Stork's bill
464. 'Sea Milkwort'
466. Thrift, Sea Pink
472. 'Sea Centaury'
472a. 'Small Centaury'

497. 'Common Hemp-nettle'
509. 'Marsh Woundwort'
538. 'Red Bartsia'
639. 'Spear Thistle'
641. Creeping Thistle

d. Seashore Plants with Blue, Pale Blue or Bluish-Purple Flowers

236. Sea Rocket
346. 'Sea Pea'
408. Sea Holly
467. 'Lax-flowered Sea Lavender'

470. 'Field Gentian
488. 'Northern Shore wort'
517. Woody Nightshade

576. Lamb's Lettuce, Corn Salad
592. 'Sea Aster'

e. Seashore Plants with Greenish or Brownish Flowers

140. 'Curled Dock'
148. 'Knotgrass'
154. Fat Hen
155. 'Shore Orache'
156. 'Hastate Orache'
157. 'Common Orache'

158. Saltwort
159. 'Herbaceous Seablite'
160. Marsh Samphire
212. Mouse-tail
421. 'Seashore Angelica'
555. 'Great Plantain'

556. 'Sea Plantain'
559. Buck's-horn Plan-tain
621. 'Field Southern-wood'
623. 'Sea Wormwood'

f. Grasses and Grass-like Plants

18. 'Sea Arrow-grass'
43. Toad Rush
49. Reed

56. Red Fescue
58. Meadow-grass
71. Lyme Grass
72. 'Bushgrass'

74a. Creeping Bent
77. 'Marsh Foxtail'
82. Couch Grass
88. 'Sea Club-rush'

GROUP IV
Dune Plants

a. Dune Plants with White Flowers

168. 'Little Mouse-ear Chickweed'
255. Thale Cress

257. Whitlow Grass
261. 'Shepherd's Cress'
310. Burnet Rose

417. 'Burnet Saxifrage'
614. Yarrow, Milfoil

b. Dune Plants with Yellow Flowers

200. 'Lesser Meadow Rue'
269. Wall-pepper
306. 'Hoary Cinquefoil'
337. Kidney-vetch, 'Ladies' Fingers'

338. Birdsfoot
339. Birdsfoot Trefoil
525. Toadflax
567. Lady's Bedstraw
606. 'Sand Cudweed'
631. Groundsel

653. 'Cat's Ear'
655. 'Autumnal Hawkbit'
658. 'Field Milk-Thistle'
665. Mouse-ear Hawkweed
666. Hawkweed

c. Dune Plants with Red, Pink or Reddish-Purple Flowers

145. Sheep's Sorrel
336. Hare's-foot
338. Birdsfoot
346. 'Sea Pea'

351. 'Narrow-leaved Vetch'
362. Common Stork's Bill
450. Ling, Heather

466. Thrift, Sea Pink
505. Thyme
594. 'Blue Fleabane'

d. Dune Plants with Blue, Pale Blue or Bluish-Purple Flowers

206. 'Meadow Anemone'
346. 'Sea Pea'
349. Tufted Vetch

388. Dog Violet
391. Wild Pansy
408. Sea Holly
517. Woody Nightshade

588. Harebell, Bluebell of Scotland
589. Sheep's-bit
594. 'Blue Fleabane'

e. Dune Plants with Greenish or Brownish Flowers

145. Sheep's Sorrel
178. 'Glabrous Rupturewort'

180. 'Perennial Knawel'
452. Crowberry

556. 'Sea Plantain'
598. 'Slender Cudweed'

f. Grasses and Grass-like Plants

45. Sweep's Brush
56. Red Fescue

57. Sheep's Fescue
69. Lop-grass

70. Marram Grass
71. Lyme Grass
92. 'Sand Sedge'

GROUP V
Plants from Woods and Thickets

a. Plants with White Flowers

27. Ramsons
35. 'Whorled Solomon's Seal'
36. 'Angular Solomon's Seal'
36a. Solomon's Seal
37. Lily-of-the-Valley
38. May Lily

109. Lesser Butterfly Orchid
109a. Greater Butterfly Orchid
115. 'Creeping Ladies' Tresses'
161. Greater Stitchwort
162. Wood Stitchwort

165. Chickweed
170. Thyme-leaved Sandwort
182. Nottingham Catchfly
201. Baneberry
209. Wood Anemone
228. 'Hollow Corydalis'

245. 'Large Bitter-cress'
247. Garlic Mustard, Jack-by-the-Hedge
292. Meadow-sweet
301. Wild Strawberry
315. 'Stone Bramble'
354. Wood-sorrel
398. Common Enchanter's Nightshade
410. Sanicle
411. 'Rough Chervil'
412. Cow Parsley
417. 'Burnet Saxifrage'
418. 'Upright Hedge-parsley'
419. Goutweed

420. Wild Angelica
422a. Cow-parsnip
423. *Laserpitium latifolium*
425. Hog's Fennel
433. 'One-flowered Wintergreen'
434. 'Larger Wintergreen'
435. 'Common Wintergreen'
447. Cowberry, Red Whortleberry
448. 'Bog Whortleberry'
449. Bilberry, Blaeberry Whortleberry
463. Chickweed Wintergreen

474. *Cynanchum vincetoxicum*
476. Bellbine, Larger Bindweed
497. 'Large-flowered Hemp-nettle'
539. Eyebright
562. Sweet Woodruff
563. 'Northern Bedstraw'
564. 'Heath Bedstraw'
566. 'Hedge Bedstraw'
568. Cleavers
575. 'Linnaea'
578. 'Elder-leaved Valerian'

b. Plants with Yellow Flowers

31. 'Yellow Star-of-Bethlehem'
101. Lady's Slipper
198. 'Common Meadow Rue'
210. 'Yellow Wood Anemone'
217. Goldilocks
218. Meadow Buttercup
220. Lesser Celandine
221. 'Creeping Buttercup'
266. Orpine
280. 'Alternate-leaved Saxifrage'
294. Herb Bennet

305. Common Tormentil
320. Broom
341. Milk-vetch
369. Touch-me-not
369a. Small Balsam
436. Yellow Bird's Nest
455. Primrose
456. Oxlip, Paigle
458. Cowslip, Paigle
460. 'Yellow Loosestrife'
461. Creeping Jenny
501. Yellow Archangel
540. 'Common Cow-wheat'
541. 'Wood Cow-wheat'

542. 'Forest Glade Cow-wheat'
593. Golden-rod
607. 'Willow-leaved Inula'
628. 'Wood Groundsel'
643. 'Cabbage Thistle'
650. Nipplewort
651. 'Wall Lettuce'
657. 'Dwarf Scorzonera'
664. 'Marsh Hawk's-beard'
665. Mouse-ear Hawkweed
666. Hawkweed
667. Common Hawkweed

c. Plants with Red, Pink or Reddish-Purple Flowers

28. 'Sand Leek'
29. 'Field Garlic'
105. Early Purple Orchis
106a. Soldier Orchis
108. Spotted Orchis
110. 'Broad Helleborine'
144. Sorrel
145. Sheep's Sorrel
150. Water-pepper
186. Red Campion

228. 'Hollow Corydalis'
229. 'Small Corydalis'
246. 'Coral-wort'
295. Water Avens
331. Zigzag Clover
345. 'Bitter Vetch'
347. 'Narrow-leaved Everlasting Pea'
348. 'Spring Pea'
355. 'Bloody Cranesbill'

356. 'Wood Cranesbill'
358. Herb Robert
399. Broad-leaved Willow-herb
400. Great Hairy Willow-herb
404. Rosebay
418. 'Upright Hedge Parsley'
420. Wild Angelica

435.	'Common Winter-green'	478.	Dodder	575.	'Linnaea'
447.	Cowberry, Red Whortleberry	497.	'Common Hemp-nettle'	578.	'Valerian'
				591.	Hemp Agrimony
448.	'Bog Whortleberry'	506.	Marjoram	634b.	'Common Burdock'
449.	Bilberry, Blaeberry Whortleberry	508.	'Hedge Woundwort'	637.	'Welted Thistle'
		511.	Wild Basil	639.	'Spear Thistle'
450	Ling	543.	'Crested Cow-wheat'	642.	Melancholy Thistle
		552.	Toothwort	645.	'Saw-wort'
				647.	'Greater Knapweed'

d. Plants with Blue, Pale Blue or Bluish-Purple Flowers

191.	'Garden Pink	388.	Dog Violet	517.	Woody Nightshade
211.	'Blue Anemone	482b.	Wood Forget-me-not	529.	'Ivy Speedwell'
345.	'Bitter Vetch'			533.	'Germander Speed-well'
348.	'Spring Pea'	484.	Common Forget-me not,		
349.	Tufted Vetch		Scorpion Grass	536.	'Common Speed-well'
352.	'Bush Vetch'	492.	Lungwort		
353.	'Wood Vetch'	493.	Bugle	539.	Eyebright
356.	'Wood Cranesbill'	494.	Pyramidal Bugle	579.	Devil's-bit Scabious
385.	'Hairy Violet'	495.	Skull-cap	583.	'Large Campanula'
386.	Sweet Violet	496.	Self-heal	584.	Bats-in-the-Belfry
387.	'Common Violet'	504.	Ground Ivy	588.	Harebell, Bluebell of Scotland
387a.	Pale Wood Violet				

e. Plants with Greenish or Brownish Flowers

9.	Lords-and-Ladies	138.	Stinging Nettle	422.	'Siberian Cow Par-snip'
32.	Herb Paris	144.	Sorrel		
110.	'Broad Helleborine'	145.	Sheep's Sorrel	432.	'Serrated Winter-green'
112.	Coral-root	150.	Water-pepper		
113.	Twayblade	266.	Orpine, Livelong	452.	Crowberry
114.	Lesser Twayblade	298.	Lady's Mantle	523.	Figwort
116.	Bird's-nest Orchid	341.	Milk-vetch	574.	Moschatel
136.	Hop	366.	Dog's Mercury	603.	'Wood Cudweed'
				622.	Mugwort

f. Grasses and Grasslike Plants

41.	'Compact Rush'	58.	Meadow-grass	72.	'Bushgrass'
42.	Soft Rush	58a.	Rough Meadowgrass	73.	'Purple Smallreed'
44.	'Hairy Woodrush'	59.	'Annual Poa'	74.	'Common Bent Grass'
47.	'Purple Moorgrass'	60.	'Wood Poa'		
48.	Mat-grass	61.	Cock's-foot	75.	'Wood Millet'
50.	Wood Melick	64a.	Meadow Oat-grass	80.	'Sweet Vernal Grass'
51.	'Mountain Melick'	65.	'False Oat-grass'	85.	Hare's-tail
55a.	Tall Brome, Giant Fescue	66.	'Tufted Hair Grass'	89.	'Wood Club-rush'
		67.	'Wavy Hair Grass'	92.	'Sand Sedge'
56.	Red Fescue	68.	Yorkshire Fog	97.	'Fingered Sedge'
57.	Sheep's Fescue	68a.	Creeping Softgrass	98.	'Pill-headed Sedge'

GROUP VI
Plants of Heaths and Moors

a. Plants with White Flowers

- 38. May Lily
- 109. Lesser Butterfly Orchis
- 208. 'Spring Pasque Flower'
- 261. 'Shepherd's Cress'
- 384. Sundew
- 405. 'Dwarf Cornel'
- 417. 'Burnet Saxifrage'
- 434. 'Larger Winter-green'
- 447. 'Cowberry'
- 448. 'Bog Whortleberry'
- 449. Whortleberry
- 463. Chickweed Winter-green
- 539. Eyebright
- 564. 'Heath Bedstraw'
- 600. 'Cat's-foot'

b. Plants with Yellow Flowers

- 34. Bog Asphodel
- 305. Common Tormentil
- 318. Dyer's Greenweed
- 319. Petty Whin
- 320. Broom
- 339. Birdsfoot Trefoil
- 380. 'Imperforate St. John's Wort'
- 540. 'Common Cow-wheat'
- 545. Yellow-rattle
- 593. Golden-rod
- 606. 'Sand Cudweed'
- 633. 'Mountain Arnica'
- 653. 'Cat's Ear'
- 654. 'Spotted Cat's Ear'
- 657. 'Dwarf Scorzonera'
- 665. Mouse-ear Hawk-weed
- 666. Hawkweed

c. Plants with Red, Pink or Reddish-Purple Flowers

- 108. Spotted Orchis
- 145. Sheep's Sorrel
- 336. Hare's-foot
- 345. 'Bitter Vetch'
- 404. Rosebay
- 405. 'Dwarf Cornel'
- 443. 'Marsh Andromeda'
- 445. Bearberry
- 446. Cranberry
- 447. Cowberry
- 448. 'Bog Whortle berry'
- 449. Whortleberry
- 450. Ling
- 451. Cross-leaved Heath
- 505. Wild Thyme
- 548. Lousewort
- 600. 'Cat's-foot'

d. Plants with Blue, Pale Blue or Bluish-Purple Flowers

- 345. Bitter Vetch
- 388. Dog Violet
- 391. Wild Pansy
- 469. 'Marsh Gentian'
- 470. 'Field Gentian'
- 536. 'Common Speed-well'
- 539. Eyebright
- 554. Common Butterwort
- 579. Devil's-bit Scabious
- 588. Harebell, Bluebell of Scotland

e. Plants with Greenish or Brownish Flowers

- 145. Sheep's Sorrel
- 178. 'Glabrous Rupture-wort'
- 180. 'Perennial Knawel'
- 409. Pennywort
- 452. Crowberry
- 555. 'Great Plantain'
- 560. Shore-weed
- 603. 'Wood Cudweed'

f. Grasses and Grasslike Plants

- 41. 'Compact Rush'
- 42. Soft Rush
- 45. Sweep's Brush

47. 'Purple Moor-grass'	70. Marram Grass	91. 'White Beak-Sedge'
48. Mat-grass	72. 'Bushgrass'	92. 'Sand Sedge'
56. Red Fescue	85. Hare's-tail	93. 'Common Sedge'
57. Sheep's Fescue	86. 'Common Cotton	95. Carnation Grass
67. 'Wavy Hair Grass'	Grass'	98. 'Pill-headed Sedge'

GROUP VII

Plants from Grassy, Uncultivated Fields and Downs (Common Pastures, and on Roadsides and Marshland)

a. Plants with White Flowers

109. Lesser Butterfly Orchid	254. 'Hairy Rock-cress'	417. 'Burnet Saxifrage'
164. 'Lesser Stichwort'	255. Thale Cress	418. 'Upright Hedge-parsley'
167. 'Field Mouse-ear Chickweed'	257. Whitlow Grass	422a Cow-parsnip
168. 'Little Mouse-ear Chickweed'	261. 'Shepherd's Cress'	431. Wild Carrot
169. 'Common Mouse-ear Chickweed'	271. Rue-leaved Saxifrage	474. *Cynanchum vincetoxicum*
171. 'Thyme-leaved Sandwort'	176. 'Meadow Saxifrage'	477. Bindweed
182. Nottingham Catch-fly	291. Dropwort	539. Eyebright
183. Bladder Campion	301. Wild Strawberry	563. 'Northern Bedstraw'
187. White Campion	301a.'Green Wild Strawberry'	566. 'Hedge Bedstraw'
249. Hoary Alison	333. White Clover, Dutch Clover	597. Daisy
253. 'Sand Rockcress'	363. Common Milkwort	600. 'Cat's-foot'
	364. 'Purging Flax'	614. Yarrow
	411. 'Rough Chervil'	616. Marguerite, Ox-eye Daisy
	416. Caraway	

b. Plants with Yellow Flowers

104. 'Elder Orchid'	320. Broom	383. Rockrose
200. 'Lesser Meadow Rue'	324. Black Medick	424. Wild Parsnip
218. Meadow Buttercup	325. 'Sickle Medick'	458. Cowslip
222. Bulbous Buttercup	326. 'Lesser Yellow Trefoil'	483. 'Yellow and Blue Forget-me-not'
248. Tower Mustard	328. 'Golden Trefoil'	520. 'Dark Mullein'
259. 'Small Alison'	329. 'Hop Trefoil'	521. Aaron's Rod
266. Orpine	337. Ladies' Fingers	521a.Great Mullein
269. Wall-pepper	339. Birdsfoot Trefoil	525. Toadflax
293. Common Agrimony	341. Milk-vetch	544. 'Greater Yellow-rattle'
302. 'Creeping Cinque-foil'	344. 'Meadow Vetchling'	567. Lady's Bedstraw
303. Silverweed	380. 'Imperforate St John's Wort'	593. Golden-rod
304. Spring Cinquefoil	381. 'Common St John's Wort'.	606. 'Sand Cudweed'
305. Common Tormentil		
306. 'Hoary Cinquefoil'		

607. 'Willow-leaved Inula'
612. Yellow Chamolile
617. Tansy
621. 'Field Southern-wood'
625. Coltsfoot
632. Ragwort
633. 'Mountain Arnica'

636. Carline Thistle
653. 'Cat's Ear'
654. 'Spotted Cat's Ear'
655. 'Autumnal Hawkbit'
656. Goat's-beard, Jack-go-to-bed-at-noon
657. 'Dwarf Scorzonera'
660. Common Dandelion

661. 'Rough Hawk's-beard'
662. 'Bitten-off Hawk's-beard'
663a. 'Smooth Hawk's-beard'
665. Mouse-ear Hawkweed
666. Hawkweed

c. Plants with Red, Pink or Reddish-Purple Flowers

29. 'Field Garlic'
29a. Crow Garlic
104. 'Elder Orchid'
143. 'Pyramid-flowered Dock'
144. Sorrel
145. Sheep's Sorrel
148. Knotgrass
175. Sand-spurrey
189. 'Red German Catch-fly'
192. Maiden Pink
291. Dropwort
321. Restharrow
330. Red Clover
331. Zigzag Clover
336. Hare's-foot

345. 'Bitter Vetch'
347. 'Narrow-leaved Everlasting Pea'
351. 'Narrow-leaved Vetch'
355. 'Bloody Cranesbill'
361. 'Dove's-foot Cranes-bill'
362. Common Storksbill
363. Common Milkwort
416. Caraway
418. 'Upright Hedge-parsley'
450. Ling, Heather
466. Thrift
471. Common Centaury

477. Bindweed
478. Dodder
491. Hound's-tongue
505. Thyme
505a. Larger Wild Thyme
506. Wild Marjoram
511. Wild Basil
558. 'Hoary Plantain'
581. Field Scabious
594. 'Blue Fleabane'
600. Cat's-foot
614. Yarrow
638. 'Stemless Thistle'
647. 'Greater Knapweed'
648. 'Brown-rayed Knap-weed'

d. Plants with Blue, Pale Blue or Bluish-Purple Flowers

206. 'Meadow Anemone'
207. Pasque Flower
323. Lucerne
345. 'Bitter Vetch'
349. Tufted Vetch
350. Hairy Tare
357. 'Mountain Cranes-bill'
360. 'Small-flowered Cranesbill'
363. Common Milkwort
385. 'Hairy Violet'
386. Sweet Violet
388. Dog Violet
470. 'Field Gentian'

483. 'Yellow and Blue Forget-me-not'
485. 'Early Forget-me-not'
485a. Early Forget-me-not
486. Viper's Bugloss
490. Alkanet
496. Self-heal
512. Basil thyme
526. 'Spiked Speedwell'
527. 'Wall Speedwell'
531. 'Spring Speedwell'
533. 'Germander Speed-well'

534. 'Thyme-leaved Speedwell'
536. Common Speedwell
539. Eyebright
576. Lamb's Lettuce
579. Devil's-bit Scabious
580. 'Small Scabious'
581. Field Scabious
582. 'Narrow-leaved Campanula'
587. Clustered Bellflower
588. Harebell, Bluebell of Scotland
589. Sheep's-bit
594. 'Blue Fleabane'
649. Chicory

e. Plants with Greenish or Brownish Flowers

138. Stinging Nettle
143. 'Pyramid-flowered Dock'
144. Sorrel
145. Sheep's Sorrel
148. Knotgrass
180. 'Perennial Knawel'

298. Lady's Mantle
341. Milk-vetch
422. 'Siberian Cowparsnip'
452. Crowberry
555. 'Great Plantain'
556. 'Sea Plantain'

557. Ribwort
558. 'Hoary Plantain'
598. 'Slender Cudweed'
599. 'Field Cudweed'
603. 'Wood Cudweed'
621. 'Field Southern wood'
622. Mugwort

f. Grasses and Grasslike Plants

45. Field Woodrush
55. Sweep's Brush
56. Red Fescue
57. Sheep's Fescue
58. Meadow-grass
61. Cock's-foot
62. Quaking Grass
63. 'Crested Dog's-tail'

64. 'Hairy Oat'
64a. 'Meadow Oat-grass'
65. 'False Oat-grass'
67. 'Wavy Hair Grass'
68. Yorkshire Fog
69. Lop-grass
72. 'Bushgrass'
73. 'Purple Smallreed'

74. 'Common Bent Grass'
78. Timothy
78a. 'Smaller Cat's-tail'
80. 'Sweet Vernal Grass'
81. Rye Grass
82. Couch Grass
92. 'Sand Sedge'
99. 'Spring Sedge'

GROUP VIII
Weeds on Cultivated Soil

a. Plants with White Flowers

165. Chickweed
167. 'Field Mouse-ear Chickweed'
169. 'Common Mouse-ear Chickweed'
171. 'Thyme-leaved Sandwort'
177. Corn Spurrey
183. Bladder Campion
187. White Campion
249. 'Hoary Alison'
250. 'Field Penny-cress'
252. Shepherd's Purse
253. 'Sand Rock-cress'
255. Thale Cress
257. Whitlow Grass
261. 'Shepherd's Cress'

271. Rue-leaved Saxifrage
332. Alsike Clover
333. White Clover, Dutch Clover
379. 'Small Mallow'
392. 'Field Pansy'
412. Cow Parsley
413. Hemlock
414. Sweet Cicely
416. Caraway
417. Burnet Saxifrage
418. 'Upright Hedge-parsley'
419. Ground Elder
422a. 'Cow-parsnip'
430. Fool's Parsley
431. Wild Carrot

477. Bindweed
481. 'Corn Gromwell'
500. White Dead-nettle
516. 'Black Nightshade'
532. 'Field Speedwell'
566. 'Great Hedge Bedstraw'
568. Cleavers
597. Daisy
610. Gallant Soldier
610a. *Galinsoga ciliata*
611. Corn Chamomile
613. Sneezewort
614. Yarrow
616. Ox-eye Daisy
618. 'Scentless Mayweed'
620. Wild Chamomile

b. Plants with Yellow Flowers

218. Meadow Buttercup

220. Lesser Celandine

221. 'Creeping Buttercup'

224. Greater Celandine
231. Turnip
232. Charlock
233. Wild Radish
234. Treacle Mustard
235. Wall Rocket
238. Winter Cress
240. Warty Cabbage
259. 'Small Alison'
262. Flixweed
263. Hedge Mustard
264. Gold of Pleasure
266. Orpine
293. Common Agrimony
302. 'Creeping Cinque-
foil'
303. Silverweed
306. 'Hoary Cinquefoil'
322. 'Common Melilot'
324. Black Medick
326. Lesser Yellow Tre-
foil'
328. 'Golden Trefoil'
329. 'Hop Trefoil'

337. Ladies' Fingers
339. Birdsfoot Trefoil
344. 'Meadow Vetchling'
380. 'Imperforate
St John's Wort'
381. 'Common
St John's Wort'
424. Wild Parsnip
483. 'Yellow and Blue
Forget-me-not'
499. 'Large-flowered
Hemp-nettle'
518. Henbane
520. 'Dark Mullein'
521. Aaron's Rod
521a. Great Mullein
525. Toadflax
544. 'Greater Yellow-
rattle'
567. Lady's Bedstraw
609. 'Tripartite Bur-Marigold'
612. Yellow Chamomile
615. Corn Marigold

617. Tansy
624. Wormwood
625. Coltsfoot
629. 'Spring Senecio'
630. Stinking Groundsel
631. Groundsel
632. Ragwort
650. Nipplewort
653. 'Cat's Ear'
655. 'Autumnal Hawkbit'
656. Jack-go-to-bed-at-
noon
658. 'Field Milk-Thistle'
659. Sow-Thistle
659a. Prickly Thistle
660. Dandelion
661. 'Rough Hawk's-
beard'
663. 'Roof-tile Hawk's-
beard'
663a. 'Smooth Hawk's-
beard'
665. Mouse-ear Hawk-
weed

c. Plants with Red, Pink or Reddish-Purple Flowers

144. Sorrel
145. Sheep's Sorrel
148. Knotgrass
151. 'Amphibious Bistort'
152. 'Persicaria'
152a. 'Pale Persicaria'
175. Sand-spurrey
190. Soapwort
193. Corn Cockle
225. Field Poppy
226. 'Long-headed
Poppy'
227. Long Prickly-headed
Poppy
230. Common Fumitory
253. 'Sand Rock-cress'
321. Restharrow
330. Red Clover
332. Alsike Clover
336. Hare's-foot
338. Birdsfoot

351. 'Narrow-leaved
Vetch'
360. 'Small-flowered
Cranesbill'
361. 'Dove's-foot Cranes-
bill'
361a. 'Cut-leaved Cranes-
bill'
362. Common Storks Bill
378. Common Mallow
379. 'Small Mallow'
379a. 'Dwarf Mallow'
399. Broad-leaved
Willow-herb
416. Caraway
418. 'Upright Hedge-
parsley'
465. Scarlet Pimpernel
478. Dodder
491. Hound's-tongue

497. 'Common Hemp-
nettle'
498. 'Red Hemp-nettle'
502. Henbit
503. Red Dead-nettle
507. Motherwort
509. 'Marsh Woundwort'
510. Black Horehound
538. 'Red Bartsia'
558. 'Hoary Plantain'
581. Field Scabious
594. 'Blue Fleabane'
614. Yarrow
626. Butterbur
634. 'Cottony Burdock'
634a. 'Great Burdock'
635. 'Lesser Burdock'
637. 'Welted Thistle'
639. 'Spear Thistle'
641. Creeping Thistle
647. 'Greater Knapweed'

d. Plants with Blue, Pale Blue or Bluish-Purple Flowers

204. 'Forking Larkspur'
323. Lucerne
349. Tufted Vetch
350. Hairy Tare
391. Wild Pansy
480. Madwort
483. 'Yellow and Blue Forget-me-not'
484. Common Forget-me-not
485. 'Early Forget-me-not'
485a. Early Forget-me-not
486. Viper's Bugloss
487a Rough Comfrey

489. Bugloss
490. Alkanet
496. Self-heal
504. Ground Ivy
512. Basil-thyme
514. 'Corn Mint'
524. Small Toadflax
527. 'Wall Speedwell'
528. 'Buxbaum's Speedwell'
529. 'Ivy Speedwell'
531. 'Spring Speedwell'
532. 'Field Speedwell'
532a. 'Procumbent Speedwell'

533. 'Germander Speedwell'
534. 'Thyme-leaved Speedwell'
539. Eyebright
561. Field Madder
576. Lamb's Lettuce
581. Field Scabious
585. 'Creeping Campanula'
588. Harebell, Bluebell of Scotland
594. 'Blue Fleabane'
646. Cornflower
649. Chicory

e. Plants with Greenish or Brownish Flowers

137. Small Nettle
138. Stinging Nettle
140. 'Curled Dock'
141. 'Broad-leaved Dock'
142. 'Long-leaved Dock'
144. Sorrel
145. Sheep's Sorrel
148. Knotgrass, Knotweed
149. Black Bindweed
150. Water-pepper
152a. 'Pale Persicaria'
153. Good King Henry
154. Fat Hen
156. 'Hastate Orache'

157. 'Common Orache'
174. 'Procumbent Pearl-wort'
178. 'Glabrous Rupturewort'
179. 'Annual Knawel'
180. 'Perennial Knawel'
212. Mouse-tail
237. Narrow-leaved Pepperwort
298. Lady's Mantle
299. Parsley Piert
367. 'Petty Spurge'
368. Sun Spurge

422. 'Siberian Cow Parsnip'
555. 'Great Plantain'
557. Ribwort
558. 'Hoary Plantain'
595. 'Canadian Fleabane'
598. 'Slender Cudweed'
599. 'Field Cudweed'
602. 'Marsh Cudweed'
603. 'Wood Cudweed'
619. 'Rayless Mayweed'
621. 'Field Southernwood'
622. Mugwort
624. Wormwood

f. Grasses and Grasslike Plants

40. 'Jointed Rush'
41. 'Compact Rush'
42. Soft Rush
43. Toad Rush
45. Sweep's Brush
55. 'Meadow Fescue'
56. 'Red Fescue'
58. Meadow-grass
59. 'Annual Poa'

61. Cock's-foot
65. 'False Oat-grass'
65a. Spring Wild Oat
66. 'Tufted Hair Grass'
68. Yorkshire Fog
68a. 'Creeping Soft-grass'
69. Lop-grass
74. 'Common Bent Grass'

74a. Creeping Bent
76. 'Meadow Foxtail'
77. 'Marsh Foxtail'
78. Timothy
80. 'Sweet Vernal Grass'
81. Rye Grass
82. Couch Grass
84. 'Wall Barley'

1. *Pinus sylvestris*, Scots Pine
2. *Picea abies*, Norway Spruce
3. *Juniperus communis*, Juniper
4. *Taxus baccata*, Yew

5. *Typha latifolia*, 'Great Reedmace'
6. *Sparganum erectum*, 'Bur-reed'
7. *Sparganum simplex*, 'Unbranched Bur-reed'
8. *Calla palustris*
9. *Arum maculatum*, Lords and Ladies
10. *Acorus calamus*, Sweet Flag

11. *Lemna trisulca*, 'Ivy Duckweed'
12. *Lemna minor*, Duckweed
13. *Lemna polyrrhiza*, 'Great Duckweed'
14. *Sagittaria sagittifolia*, Arrow-head
15. *Alisma plantago-aquatica*, Water-Plantain
16. *Butomus umbellatus*, Flowering Rush

17. *Triglochin palustris,* 'Marsh Arrow-grass'
18. *Triglochin maritima,* 'Sea Arrow-grass'
19. *Scheuchzeria palustris,* 'Marsh Scheuchzeria'
20. *Potamageton natans,* 'Broad-leaved Pondweed'
21. *Potomageton gramineus,* 'Various-leaved Pondweed'
22. *Potomageton perfoliatus,* 'Perfoliate Pondweed'

23. *Elodea canadensis*, Canadian Pondweed
24. *Hydrocharis morsus-ranae*, Frog-bit
25. *Stratioides aloides*, Water Soldier
26. *Fritllaria meleagris*, Fritillary
27. *Allium ursinum*, Ramsons
28. *Allium scorodoprasum*, 'Sand Leek'

29. *Allium oleraceum*, 'Field Garlick'
30. *Allium schoenoprasum*, Chives
31. *Gagea lutea*, 'Yellow Star-of-Bethlehem'
32. *Paris quadrifolia*, Herb Paris
33. *Tofieldia pusilla*, 'Scottish Asphodel'
34. *Narthecium ossifragum*, Bog Asphodel

35. *Polygonatum verticillatum*, 'Whorled Solomon's Seal'
36. *Polygonatum odoratum*, 'Angular Solomon's Seal'
37. *Convallaria majalis*, Lily of the Valley
38. *Maianthemum bifolium*, May Lily
39. *Iris pseudacorus*, Yellow Flag

40. *Juncus articulatus*, 'Jointed Rush'
41. *Juncus glomeratus*, 'Compact Rush'
42. *Juncus effusus*, Soft Rush
43. *Juncus bufonius*, Toad Rush
44. *Luzula pilosa*, 'Hairy woodrush'

45. *Luzula campestris*, Sweep's Brush
46. *Sesleria caerulea*, 'Blue Sesleria'
47. *Molinia coerulea*, 'Purple moor-grass'
48. *Nardus stricta*, Mat Grass

49. *Phragmites communis*, Reed
50. *Melica uniflora*, Wood Melick
51. *Melica nutans*, 'Mountain Melick'
52. *Glyceria fluitans*, Flote Grass
53. *Glyceria maxima*, Reed-grass
54. *Phalaris arundinacea*, Reed-grass
55. *Festuca pratensis*, 'Meadow Fescue'

56. *Festuca rubra*, 'Creeping Fescue'
57. *Festuca ovina*, Sheep's Fescue
58. *Poa pratensis*, Meadow-grass
59. *Poa annua*, 'Annual Poa'

60. *Poa nemoralis*, 'Wood Poa'
61. *Dactylis glomerata*, Cock's-foot
62. *Briza media*, Quaking Grass
63. *Cynosurus cristatus*, 'Crested Dog's-tail'

64. *Avena pubescens*, 'Hairy Oat'
65. *Avena elatior*, 'False Oat Grass'
66. *Deschampsia caespitosa*, 'Tufted hair-grass'
67. *Deschampsia flexuosa*, 'Wavy hair-grass'
68. *Holcus lanatus*, Yorkshire Fog
69. *Bromus mollis*, Lop-grass

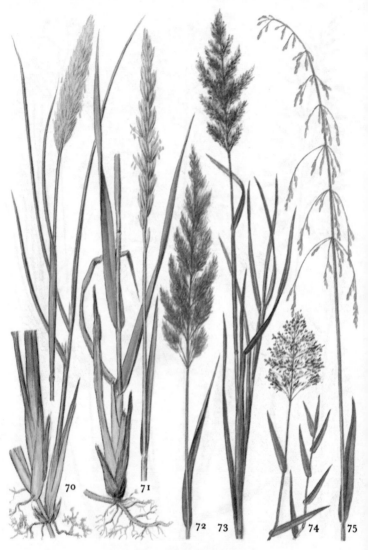

70. *Ammophila arenaria*, Marram Grass
71. *Elymus arenarius*, Lyme-grass
72. *Calamagrostis epigejos*, 'Bushgrass'
73. *Calamagrostis canescens*, 'Purple Smallreed'
74. *Agrostis tenuis*, 'Common Bent-grass'
75. *Milium effusum*, 'Wood Millet'

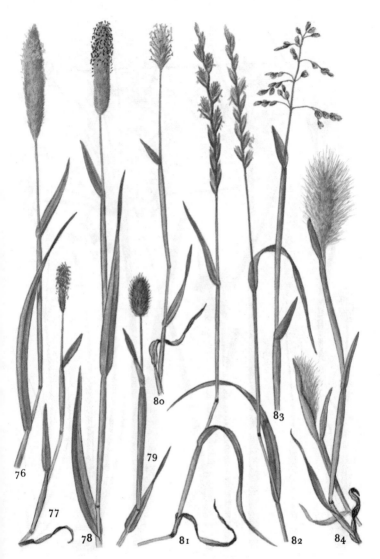

76. *Alopecurus pratensis,* 'Meadow Fox-tail'
77. *Alopecurus geniculatus,* 'Marsh Fox-tail'
78. *Phleum pratense,* Timothy
79. *Phleum commatatum,* 'Alpine Cats-tail'
80. *Anthoxanthum odoratum,* 'Sweet Vernal-grass'
81. *Lolium perenne,* Rye-grass
82. *Agropyron repens,* Couch Grass
83. *Hierochloe odorata,* Holy-grass
84. *Hordeum murinum,* 'Wall Barley'

85. *Eriophorum vaginatum*, Hare's-tail
86. *Eriophorum angustifolium*, 'Common
    Cotton-grass'
87. *Scirpus lacustris*, Bulrush
88. *Scirpus maritimus*, 'Sea Club-rush'

89. *Scirpus sylvaticus*, 'Wood Club-rush'
90. *Eleocharis palustris*, 'Common Spike
    rush'
91. *Rhyncospora alba*, 'White Beak-
    sedge'

92. *Carex arenaria*, 'Sand Sedge'
93. *Carex nigra*, 'Common Sedge'
94. *Carex acuta*, 'Tufted Sedge'
95. *Carex panicea*, Carnation Grass
96. *Carex curta*, 'White Sedge'

97. *Carex digitata*, 'Fingered Sedge'
98. *Carex pilulifera*, 'Pill-headed Sedge'
99. *Carex caryophyllea*, 'Spring Sedge'
100. *Carex rostrata*, 'Beaked Sedge'

101. *Cypripedium calceolus*, Lady's Slipper
102. *Ophyris insectifera*, Fly Orchid
103. *Gymnadenia conopsea*, Fragrant Orchid
104. *Orchis sambucina*, 'Elder Orchid'
105. *Orchis mascula*, Early Purple Orchis

106. *Orchis militaris*, 'Soldier Orchis'
107. *Orchis strictifolia*, Meadow Orchis
108. *Orchis maculata*, Spotted Orchis
109. *Platanthera bifolia*, Lesser Butterfly Orchis
110. *Epipactis helleborina*, 'Broad Helleborine'

111. *Epipactis palustris*, 'Marsh Helleborine'
112. *Coralorrhiza trifida*, Coral-root
113. *Listera ovata*, Twayblade
114. *Listera cordata*, Lesser Twayblade
115. *Goodyera repens*, 'Creeping Lady's Tresses'
116. *Neottia nidus-avis*, Bird's-nest Orchid

117. *Populus tremula*, Aspen
118. *Salix pentandra*, Bay Willow
119. *Salix caprea*, Goat Willow
120. *Salix cinerea*, Common Sallow

121. *Salix aurita*, 'Eared Sallow'
122. *Salix laponum*, 'Downy Willow'
123. *Salix repens*, 'Creeping Willow'
124. *Salix herbacea*, 'Least Willow'
125. *Salix reticulata*, 'Reticulate Willow'
126. *Myrica gale*, Bog Myrtle

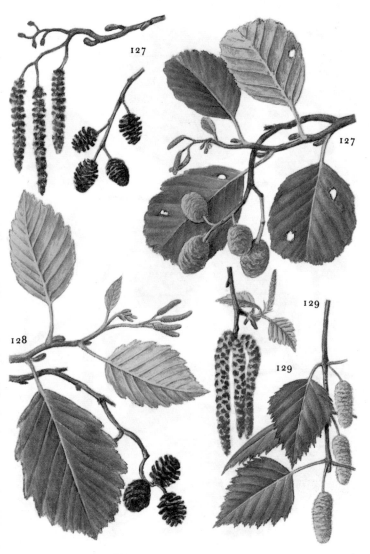

127. *Alnus glutinosa*, Alder
128. *Alnus incana*, 'Grey Alder'
129. *Betula verrucosa*, Silver Birch

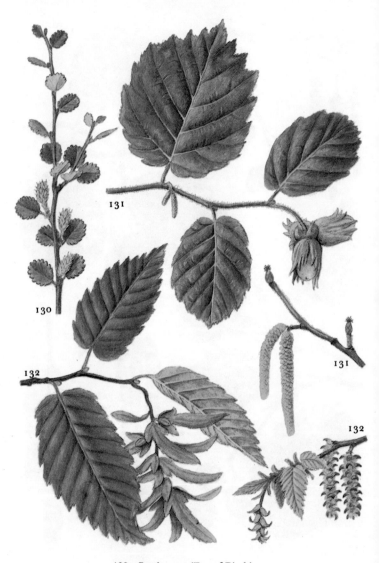

130. *Betula nana*, 'Dwarf Birch'
131. *Corylus avellana*, Hazel
132. *Carpinus betulus*, Hornbeam

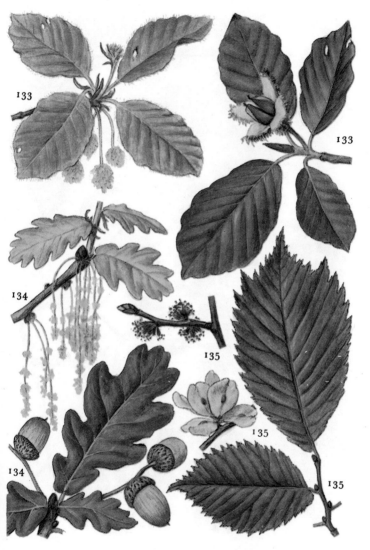

133. *Fagus sylvatica*, Beech
134. *Quercus robur*, Common Oak
135. *Ulmus glabra*, Wych Elm

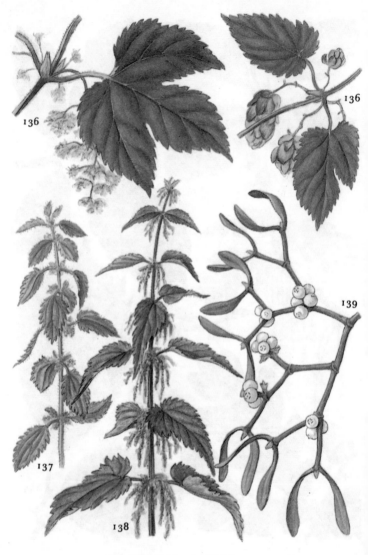

136. *Humulus lupulus*, Hop
137. *Urtica urens*, Small Nettle
138. *Urtica dioica*, Stinging Nettle
139. *Viscum album*, Mistletoe

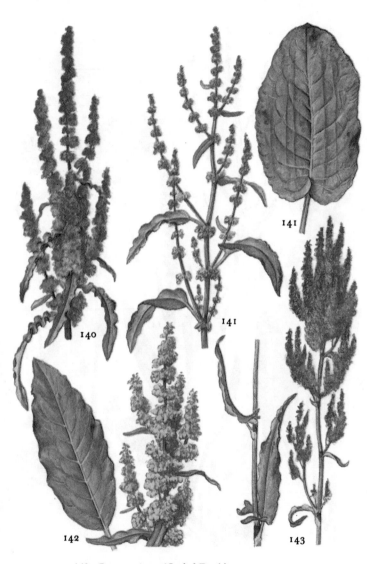

140. *Rumex crispus*, 'Curled Dock'
141. *Rumex obtusifolius*, 'Broad-leaved Dock'
142. *Rumex domesticus*, 'Long-leaved Dock'
143. *Rumex thrysiflorus*, 'Pyramid-flowered Dock'

144. *Rumex acetosa*, Sorrel
145. *Rumex acetosella*, Sheep's Sorrel
146. *Oxyria digyna*, Mountain Sorrel
147. *Polygonum viviparum*, 'Viviparous Polygonum'
148. *Polygonum aviculare*, Knotgrass
149. *Polygonum convolvulus*, Black Bindweed

150. *Polygonum hydropeper*, Water-pepper
151. *Polygonum amphibium*, 'Amphibious Bistort'
152. *Polygonum persicaria*, 'Persicaria'
153. *Chenopodium bonus-henricus*, Good King Henry
154. *Chenopodium album*, Fat Hen

155. *Atriplex littoralis*, 'Shore Orache'
156. *Atriplex hastata*, 'Hastate Orache'
157. *Atriplex patula*, 'Common Orache'
158. *Salsola kali*, Saltwort
159. *Suaeda maritima*, 'Herbaceous Seablight'
160. *Salicornia europea*, Marsh Samphire

161. *Stellaria holostea*, Stitchwort
162. *Stellaria nemorum*, Wood Stitchwort
163. *Stellaria palustris*, 'Marsh Stitchwort'
164. *Stellaria graminea*, 'Lesser Stitchwort'
165. *Stellaria media*, Chickweed

166. *Cerastium alpinum*, 'Alpine Mouse-ear Chickweed'
167. *Cerastium arvense*, 'Field Mouse-ear Chickweed'
168. *Cerastium semidecandrum*, 'Little Mouse-ear Chickweed'
169. *Cerastium caespitosum*, 'Common Mouse-ear Chickweed'
170. *Arenaria trinerva*, 'Thyme-leaved Sandwort'
171. *Arenaria serpyllifolia*, 'Lesser, Thyme-leaved Sandwort'
172. *Honckenya peploides*, 'Sea Sandwort'

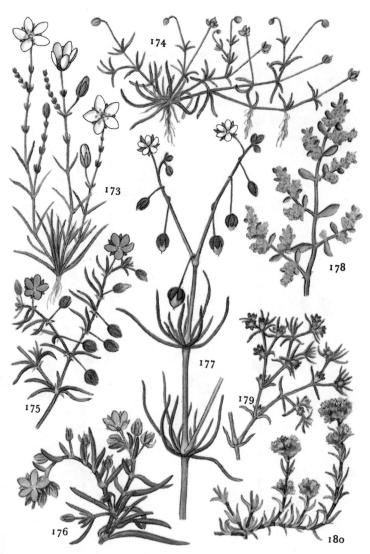

173. *Sagina nodosa*, 'knotted Pearlwort'
174. *Sagina procumbens*, 'Procumbent Pearlwort'
175. *Spergularia rubra*, Sand-spurrey
176. *Spergularia salina*, Sea Sand-spurrey

177. *Spergularia arvensis*, Corn Spurrey
178. *Herniaria glabra*, 'Glabrous Rupture-wort'
179. *Scleranthus annuus*, 'Annual Knawel'
180. *Scleranthus perennis*, 'Perennial Knawel'

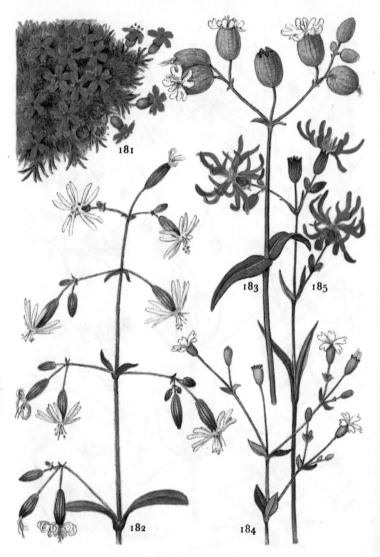

181. *Silene acaulis,* Moss Campion
182. *Silene nutans,* Nottingham Catchfly
183. *Silene cucubalus,* Bladder Campion
184. *Silene rupestris,* 'Rock Campion'
185. *Lychnis flos-cuculi,* Ragged Robin

186. *Melandrium rubrum*, Red Campion
187. *Melandrium album*, White Campion
188. *Viscaria alpina*, 'Red Alpine Catchfly'
189. *Viscaria vulgaris*, 'Red German Catchfly'

190. *Saponaria officinalis*, Soapwort
191. *Dianthus superbus*, 'Garden Pink'
192. *Dianthus deltoides*, Maiden Pink
193. *Agrostemma githago*, Corn Cockle

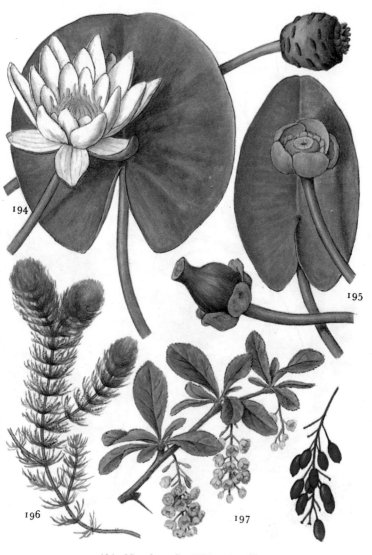

194. *Nymphaea alba*, White Waterlily
195. *Nuphar lutea*, Yellow Water-lily
196. *Ceratophyllum demersum*, Hornwort
197. *Berberis vulgaris*, Barberry

198. *Thalictrum flavum*, 'Common Meadow Rue'
199. *Thalictrum alpinum*, 'Alpine Meadow Rue'
200. *Thalictrum dunense*, 'Lesser Meadow Rue'
201. *Actaea spicata*, Baneberry

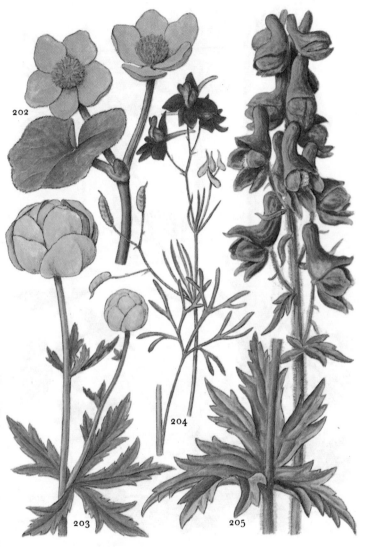

202. *Caltha palustris*, Kingcup
203. *Trollius europaeus*, 'Globe Flower'
204. *Delphinium consolida*, 'Forking Larkspur'
205. *Aconitum septentrionale*, Northern Monkshood

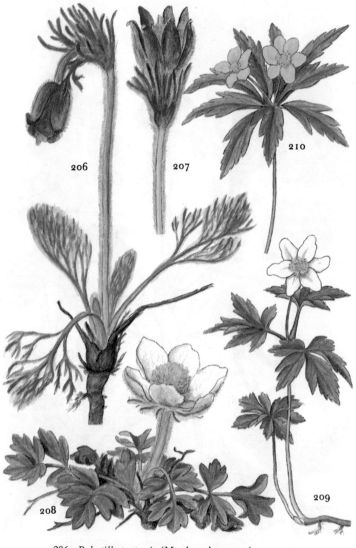

206. *Pulsatilla pratensis*, 'Meadow Anemone'
207. *Pulsatilla vulgaris*, 'Pasque Flower'
208. *Pulsatilla vernalis*, 'Spring Pasque Flower'
209. *Anemone nemorosa*, Wood anemone
210. *Anemone ranunculoides*, 'Yellow Wood Anemone'

211. *Anemone hepatica*, 'Blue Anemone'
212. *Myosurus minimus*, Mouse-tail
213. *Batrachium aquatile*, 'Water Crowfoot'
214. *Ranunculus pygmaeus*, 'Pygmy Ranunculus'
215. *Ranunculus glacialis*, 'Ice Ranunculus'

216. *Ranunculus lingua*, Great Spearwort
217. *Ranunculus auricomus*, Goldilocks
218. *Ranunculus acris*, Meadow Buttercup
219. *Ranunculus flammula*, Lesser Spearwort

220. *Ranunculus ficaria*, Lesser Celandine
221. *Ranunculus repens*, 'Creeping Buttercup'
222. *Ranunculus bulbosus*, 'Bulbous Buttercup'
223. *Ranunculus sceleratus*, 'Celery-leaved Crowfoot'

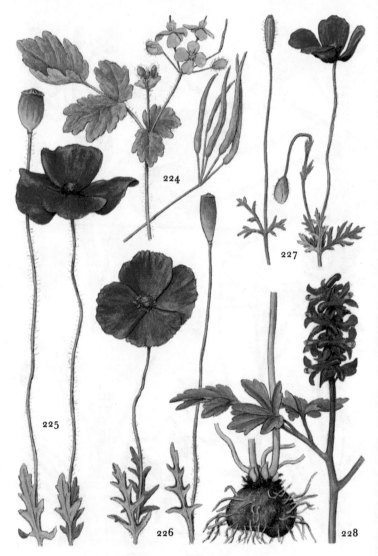

224. *Chelidonium majus*, Greater Celandine
225. *Papaver rhoeas*, Field Poppy
226. *Papaver dubium*, 'Long-head Poppy'
227. *Papaver argemone*, Long Prickly-headed Poppy
228. *Corydalis cava*, 'Hollow Corydalis'

229. *Corydalis fabacea*, 'Small Corydalis'
230. *Fumaria officinalis*, Common Fumitory
231. *Brassica campestris*, Turnip
232. *Sinapis arvensis*, Charlock
233. *Raphanus raphaniastrum*, Wild radish

234. *Erysimum cheiranthoides*, Treacle Mustard
235. *Diplotaxis muralis*, Wall Rocket
236. *Cakile maritima*, Sea Rocket
237. *Lepidium ruderale*, Narrow-leaved Pepper
238. *Barbarea vulgaris*, Winter Cress

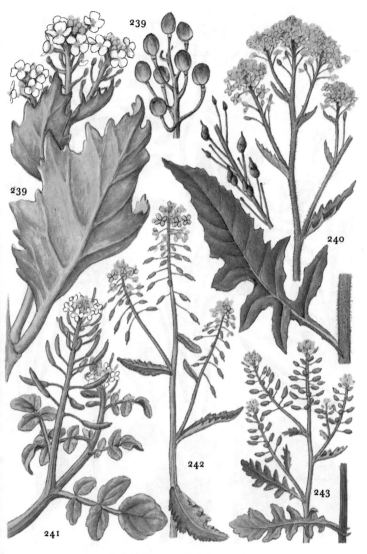

239. *Crambe maritima,* Seakale
240. *Bunias orientalis,* 'Warty Cabbage'
241. *Nasturtium microphyllum,* Watercress
242. *Rorippa amphibia,* 'Great Yellow Cress'
243. *Rorippa islandica,* 'Marsh Yellow-cress'

244. *Cardamine pratensis*, Lady's Smock
245. *Cardamine amara*, 'Large Bitter-cress'
246. *Dentaria bulbifera*, 'Coral-wort'
247. *Alliaria petiolata*, Jack-by-the-Hedge
248. *Turritis glabra*, Tower Mustard

249. *Berteroa incana*, 'Hoary Alison'
250. *Thlaspi arvense*, 'Field Penny-cress'
251. *Thlaspi alpestre*, 'Alpine Penny-cress'
252. *Capsella bursa-pastoris*, Shepherd's Purse
253. *Arabis arenosa*, 'Sand Rock-cress'
254. *Arabis hirsuta*, 'Hairy Rock-cress'

255. *Arabidopsis thaliana*, Thale Cress
256. *Draba alpina*, Alpine Whitlow Grass
257. *Erophila verna*, Whitlow Grass
258. *Subularia aquatica*, Awlwort
259. *Alyssum alyssoides*, 'Small Alison'
260. *Cochlearia officinalis*, Scurvy Grass
261. *Teesdalia nudicaulis*, 'Shepherd's Cress'
262. *Sisymbrium sophia*, Flixweed

263. *Sisymbrium officinale,* Hedge Mustard
264. *Camelia sativa,* Gold of Pleasure
265. *Sedum album,* 'White Stonecrop'
266. *Sedum telephium,* Orpine
267. *Sedum rosea,* Rose-root

268. *Sedum annuum*, 'Annual Stonecrop'
269. *Sedum acre*, Wall-pepper
270. *Saxifraga oppositifolia*, Purple Saxifrage
271. *Saxifraga tridactylites*, Rue-leaved Saxifrage
272. *Saxifraga aizoides*, 'Yellow Mountain Saxifrage'
273. *Saxifraga nivalis*, 'Alpine Saxifrage'
274. *Saxifraga rivularis*, 'Brook Saxifrage'
275. *Saxifraga stellaris*, 'Starry Saxifrage'

276. *Saxifraga granulata*, 'Meadow Saxifrage'
277. *Saxifraga cotyledon*, 'Cup Saxifrage'
278. *Saxifraga cernua*, 'Drooping Saxifrage'
279. *Parnassia palustris*, Grass of Parnassus
280. *Chrysosplenum alternifolium*, 'Alternate-leaved Saxifrage'

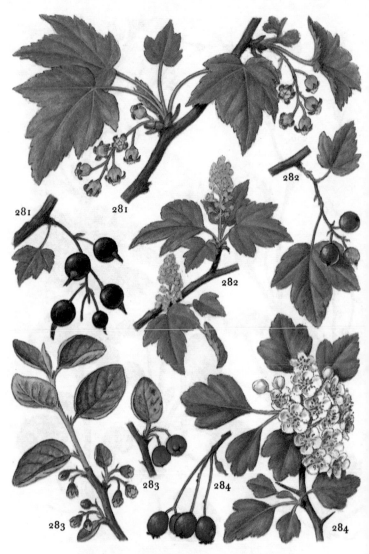

281. *Ribes nigrum*, Black Currant
282. *Ribes alpinum*, 'Mountain Currant'
283. *Cotoneaster integerrima*, 'Great Orme Berry'
284. *Crataegus oxyacantha*, Hawthorn

285. *Sorbus aucuparia,* Mountain Ash
286. *Sorbus intermedia,* 'Cut-leaved White Beam'
287. *Malus sylvestris,* Crab Apple

288. *Prunus spinosa*, Blackthorn
289. *Prunus padus*, Bird Cherry
290. *Prunus avium*, Wild Cherry

291. *Filipendula vulgaris,* Dropwort
292. *Filipendula ulmaria,* Meadow-Sweet
293. *Agrimonia eupatoria,* Common Agrimony
294. *Geum urbanum,* Herb Bennet

295. *Geum rivale*, Water Avens
296. *Dryas octopetala*, 'Mountain Avens'
297. *Alchemilla alpina*, 'Alpine Lady's-Mantle'
298. *Alchemilla vulgaris*, Lady's Mantle
299. *Aphanes arvensis*, Parsley Piert
300. *Sibbaldia procumbens*, 'Least Cinquefoil'

301. *Fragaria vesca*, Wild Strawberry
302. *Potentilla reptans*, 'Creeping Cinquefoil'
303. *Potentilla anserina*, Silverweed
304. *Potentilla verna*, Spring Cinquefoil
305. *Potentilla erecta*, Common Tormentil

306. *Potentilla argentea*, 'Hoary Cinquefoil'
307. *Potentilla norvegica*, 'Norwegian Cinquefoil'
308. *Potentilla fruticosa*, Shrubby Cinquefoil
309. *Comarum palustre*, 'Marsh Cinquefoil'
310. *Rosa spinosissima*, Burnet Rose

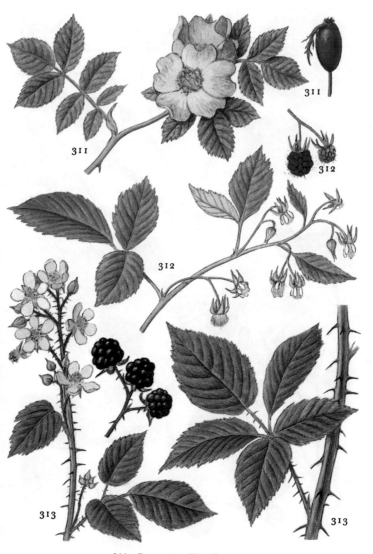

311. *Rosa canina*, Dog Rose
312. *Rubus idaeus*, Raspberry
313. *Rubus fruticosus*, Blackberry

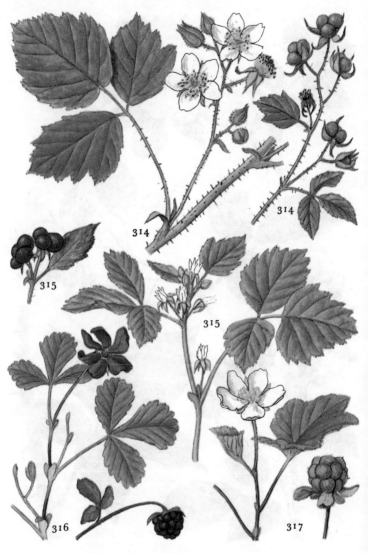

314. *Rubus caesius*, Dewberry
315. *Rubus saxatilis*, 'Stone Bramble'
316. *Rubus arcticus*, 'Arctic Stone Bramble'
317. *Rubus chamaemorus*, Cloudberry

318. *Genista tinctoria*, Dyer's Greenweed
319. *Genista anglica*, Petty Whin
320. *Sarothamnus scoparius*, Broom
321. *Ononis repens*, Rest-harrow
322. *Melilotus officinialis*, 'Common Melilot'

323. *Medicago sativa,* Lucerne
324. *Medicago lupulina,* Black Medick
325. *Medicago falcata,* 'Sickle Medick'
326. *Trifolium dubium,* 'Lesser Yellow Trefoil'

327. *Trifolium spadicium,* 'Brown Clover'
328. *Trifolium aureum,* 'Golden Trefoil'
329. *Trifolium campestre,* 'Hop Trefoil'

330. *Trifolium pratense,* Red Clover
331. *Trifolium medium,* Zigzag Clover
332. *Trifolium hybridum,* Alsike Clover
333. *Trifolium repens,* Dutch Clover
334. *Trifolium montanum,* 'Mountain Clover'

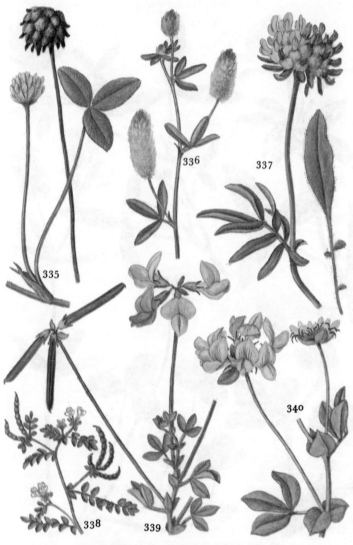

335. *Trifolium fragiferum*, 'Strawberry Clover'
336. *Trifolium arvense*, Hare's Foot
337. *Anthyllis vulneraria*, Ladies' Fingers
338. *Ornithopus perpusillus*, Birdsfoot
339. *Lotus corniculatus*, Birdsfoot trefoil
340. *Lotus uliginosus*, Large Birdsfoot-trefoil

341. *Astragalus glycyphyllos*, Milk-vetch
342. *Astragalus alpinus*, 'Alpine Milk-vetch'
343. *Oxytropis campestris*, 'Yellow Oxytropis'
344. *Lathyrus pratensis*, 'Meadow Vetchling'
345. *Lathyrus montanus*, 'Bitter Vetch'

346. *Lathyris maritimus*, 'Sea Pea'
347. *Lathyris sylvestris*, 'Narrow-leaved Everlasting Pea'
348. *Lathyris vernus*, 'Spring Pea'
349. *Vicia cracca*, Tufted Vetch

350. *Vicia hirsuta*, Hairy Tare
351. *Vicia angustifolia*, 'Narrow-leaved Vetch'
352. *Vicia sepium*, 'Bush Vetch'
353. *Vicia sylvatica*, 'Wood Vetch'
354. *Oxalis acetosella*, Wood-sorrel

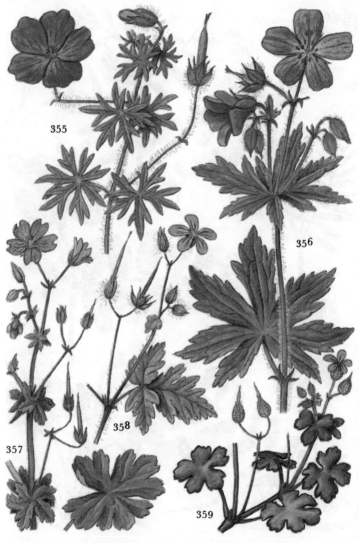

355. *Geranium sanguinium*, 'Bloody Cranesbill'
356. *Geranium sylvaticum*, 'Wood Cranesbill'
357. *Geranium pyrenaicum*, 'Mountain Cranesbill'
358. *Geranium robertianum*, Herb Robert
359. *Geranium lucidum*, 'Shining Cranesbill'

360. *Geranium pusillum*, 'Small-flowered Cranesbill'
361. *Geranium molle*, 'Dove's-foot Cranesbill'
362. *Erodium cicutarium*, Common Stork's Bill
363. *Polygala vulgaris*, Common Milkwort
364. *Linum catharticum*, 'Purging Flax'
365. *Callitriche stagnalis*, 'Stagnant Water Starwort'

366. *Mercurialis perennis*, Dog's Mercury
367. *Euphorbia peplus*, 'Petty Spurge'
368. *Euphorbia helioscopia*, Sun Spurge
369. *Impatiens noli-tangere*, Touch-me-not

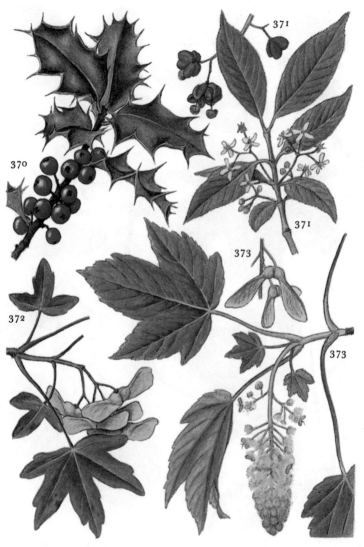

370. *Ilex aquifolium*, Holly
371. *Euonymus europaeus*, Spindle Tree
372. *Acer campestre*, Common Maple
373. *Acer pseudoplatanus*, Sycamore

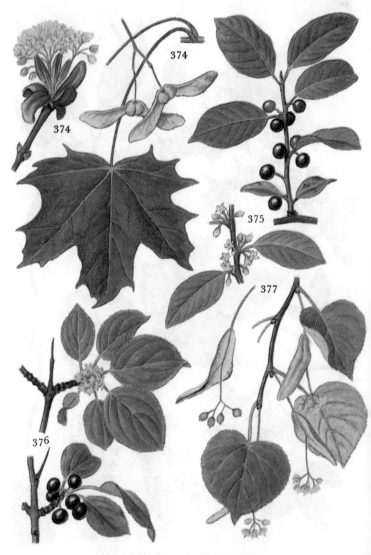

374. *Acer plantinoides*, Norway Maple
375. *Frangula alnus*. Alder Buckthorn
376. *Rhamnus cathartica*, Buckthorn
377. *Tilia cordata*, 'Small-leaved Lime'

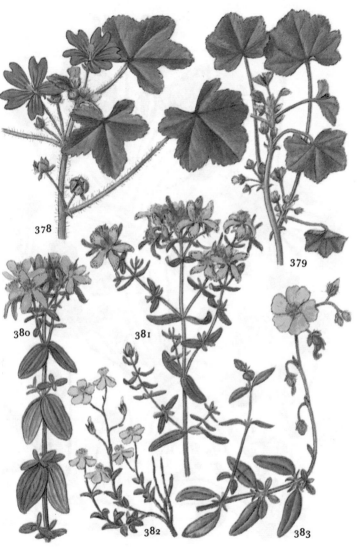

378. *Malva sylvestris*, Common Mallow
379. *Malva pusilla*, 'Small Mallow'
380. *Hypericum maculatum*, 'Imperforate St. John's Wort'
381. *Hypericum perforatum*, 'Common St. John's Wort'
382. *Helianthemum oelandicum*, 'Oeland Rock Rose'
383. *Helianthemum nummularium*, Rockrose

384. *Drosera rotundifolia*, Sundew
385. *Viola hirta*, 'Hairy Violet'
386. *Viola odorata*, Sweet Violet
387. *Viola riviniana*, 'Common Violet'
388. *Viola canina*, Dog Violet

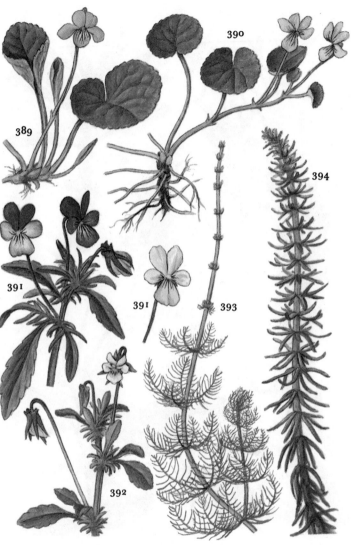

389. *Viola palustris*, 'Marsh Violet'
390. *Viola biflora*, 'Alpine Violet'
391. *Viola tricolor*, Wild Pansy
392. *Viola arvensis*, 'Field Pansy'
393. *Myriophyllum spicatum*, 'Spiked Water-milfoil'
394. *Hippuris vulgaris*, Mare's Tail

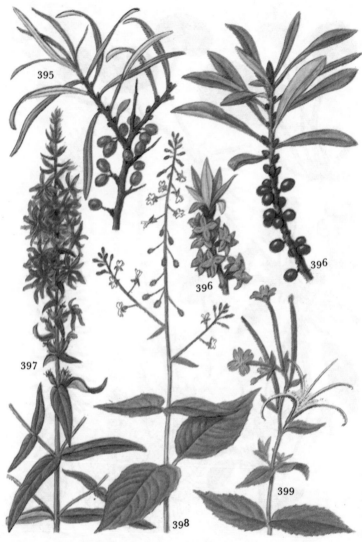

395. *Hippophae rhamnoides*, Sea Buckthorn
396. *Daphne mezereum*, Mezereon
397. *Lythrum salicaria*, Purple Loosestrife
398. *Circaea lutetiana*, Common Enchanter's Nightshade
399. *Epilobium montanum*, Broad-leaved Willow-herb

400. *Epilobium hirsutum*, Great Hairy Willow-herb
401. *Epilobium hornemannii*, 'Moss Willow-herb'
402. *Epilobium palustre*, 'Marsh Willow-herb'
403. *Epilobium anagallidifolium*, 'Alpine Willow Herb'
404. *Chamaenerion angustifolium*, Rosebay

405. *Cornus suecica*, 'Dwarf Cornel'
406. *Cornus sanguinea*, 'Dogwood'
407. *Hedera helix*, Ivy
408. *Eryngium maritimum*, Sea Holly
409. *Hydrocotyle vulgaris*, Pennywort
410. *Sanicula europaea*, Sanicle

411. *Chaerophyllum temulum*, 'Rough Chervil'
412. *Anthriscus sylvestris*, Cow Parsley
413. *Conium maculatum*, Hemlock
414. *Myrrhis odorata*, Sweet Cicely

415. *Cicuta virosa*, Cowbane
416. *Carum carvi*, Caraway
417. *Pimpinella saxifraga*, 'Burnet Saxifrage'
418. *Torilis japonica*, 'Upright Hedge Parsley'
419. *Aegopodium podagraria*, Ground Elder

420. *Angellica sylvestris*, Wild Angelica
421. *Archangelica litoralis*, 'Seashore Angelica'

422. *Heracleum sibericum*, 'Siberian Cow Parsnip'
423. *Laserpitium latifolium*

424. *Pastinaca sativa*, Wild Parsnip
425. *Peucedanum palustre*, Hog's Fennel
426. *Sium latifolium*, Water Parsnip
427. *Sium erectum*, 'Narrow-leaved Water Parsnip'
428. *Oenanthe fistulosa*, Water Dropwort

429. *Oenanthe aquatica*, 'Fine-leaved Water Dropwort'
430. *Aethusa cynapium*, Fool's Parsley
431. *Daucus carota*, Wild Carrot
432. *Pyrola secunda*, 'Serrated Wintergreen'

433. *Pyrola uniflora*, 'One-flowered Wintergreen'
434. *Pyrola rotundifolia*, 'Larger Wintergreen'
435. *Pyrola minor*, 'Common Wintergreen'
436. *Monotropa hypopitys*, Yellow Bird's Nest
437. *Rhododendron lapponicum*, 'Arctic Rhododendron'
438. *Ledum palustre*, 'Marsh Ledum'

439. *Loiseleuria decumbens,* 'Loiseleuria'
440. *Phyllodoce coerulea,* Mountain Heath
441. *Cassiope hypnoides*
442. *Cassiope tetragona*

443. *Andromeda polifolia,* 'Marsh Andromeda'
444. *Arctostaphylos alpina,* 'Black Bearberry'
445. *Arctostaphylos uva-ursi,* Bearberry
446. *Oxycoccus palustris,* Cranberry

447. *Vaccinium vitis-idaea*, Cowberry
448. *Vaccinium uliginosum*, 'Bog Whort-
    leberry'
449. *Vaccinium myrtillus*, Whortleberry

450. *Calluna vulgaris*, Ling
451. *Erica tetralix*, Cross-leaved Heath
452. *Empetrum nigrum*, Crowberry
453. *Diapensia lapponica*,

454. *Androsace septentrionalis*, 'Mountain Pimpernel'
455. *Primula vulgaris*, Primrose
456. *Primula elatior*, Oxlip
457. *Primula farinosa*, 'Bird's Eye Primrose'
458. *Primula veris*, Cowslip

459. *Hottonia palustris*, Water Violet
460. *Lysimachia vulgaris*, 'Yellow Loosestrife'
461. *Lysimachia nummularia*, Creeping Jenny
462. *Lysimachia thyrsiflora*, 'Tufted Loosestrife'
463. *Trientalis europaea*, Chickweed Wintergreen
464. *Glaux maritima*, 'Sea Milkwort'

465. *Anagalis arvensis*, Scarlet Pimpernel
466. *Armeria maritima*, Thrift
467. *Limonium humile*, 'Lax-flowered Sea Lavender'
468. *Gentiana nivalis*, 'Small Gentian'
469. *Gentiana pneumonanthe*, 'Marsh Gentian'

470. *Gentiana campestris*, 'Field Gentian'
471. *Centaurium minus*, Common Centaury
472. *Centaurium vulgare*, 'Sea Century'
473. *Menyanthes trifoliata*, Bogbean
474. *Cynanchum vincetoxicum*

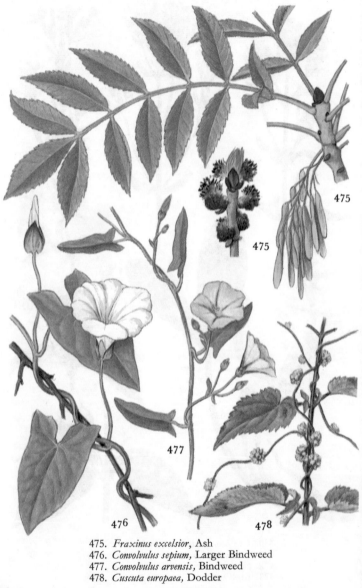

475. *Fraxinus excelsior*, Ash
476. *Convolvulus sepium*, Larger Bindweed
477. *Convolvulus arvensis*, Bindweed
478. *Cuscuta europaea*, Dodder

479. *Polemonium caeruleum*, Jacob's Ladder
480. *Asperugo procumbens*, Madwort
481. *Lithospermum arvense*, 'Corn Gromwell'
482. *Myosotis palustris*, 'Water Forget-me-not'
483. *Myosotis versicolor*, 'Yellow and Blue Forget-me-not'
484. *Myosotis arvensis*, Common Forget-me-not
485. *Myosotis stricta*, 'Early Forget-me-not'

486. *Echium vulgare*, Viper's Bugloss
487. *Symphytum officinale*, Comfrey
488. *Mertensia maritima*, 'Northern Shore-wort'
489. *Anchusa arvensis*, Bugloss
490. *Anchusa officinalis*, Alkanet

491. *Cynoglossum officinale*, Hound's Tongue
492. *Pulmonaria officinalis*, Lungwort
493. *Ajuga reptans*, Bugle
494. *Ajuga pyramidalis*, Pyramidal Bugle
495. *Scutellaria galericulata*, Skull-cap

496. *Prunella vulgaris*, Self-heal
497. *Galeopsis tetrahit*, 'Common Hemp Nettle'
498. *Galeopsis ladanum* 'Red Hemp Nettle'
499. *Galeopsis speciosa*, 'Large-flowered Hemp Nettle'
500. *Lamium album*, White Dead-Nettle

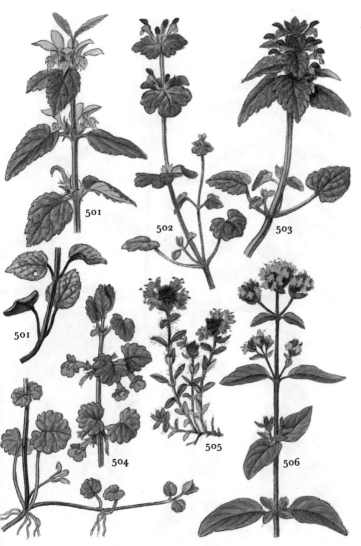

501. *Lamium galeobdolon,* Yellow Archangel
502. *Lamium amplexicaule,* Henbit
503. *Lamium purpureum,* Red Dead-Nettle
504. *Glechoma hederacea,* Ground Ivy
505. *Thymus serpiphyllum,* Wild Thyme
506. *Origanum vulgare,* Marjorum

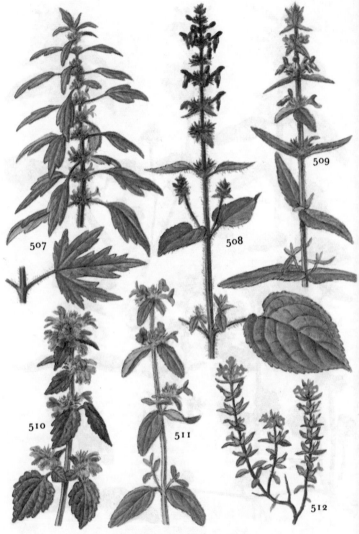

507. *Leonurus cardiaca*, Motherwort
508. *Stachys sylvatica*, 'Hedge Woundwort'
509. *Stachys palustris*, 'Marsh Woundwort'
510. *Ballota nigra*, Black Horehound
511. *Clinopodium vulgare*, Wild Basil
512. *Calamintha acinos*, Basil Thyme

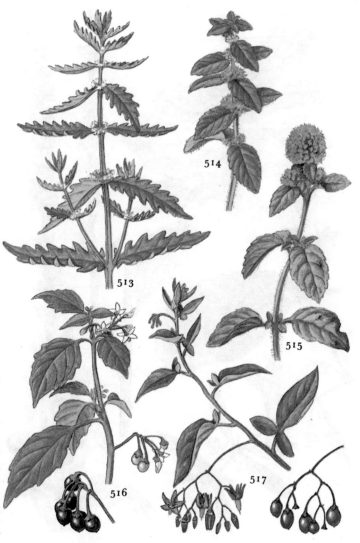

513. *Lycopus europaeus*, 'Gipsy-wort'
514. *Mentha arvensis*, 'Corn Mint'
515. *Mentha aquatica*, 'Water Mint'
516. *Solanum nigrum*, 'Black Nightshade'
517. *Solanum dulcamara*, Woody Nightshade

518. *Hyoscyamus niger*, Henbane
519. *Lycium   halimifolium*,   Duke of
     Argyll's Tea-plant
520. *Verbascum nigrum*, 'Dark Mullein'
521. *Verbascum thapsus*, Aaron's Rod

522. *Digitalis purpurea*, Foxglove
523. *Schrophularia nodosa*, Figwort
524. *Linaria minor*, 'Small Toadflax'
525. *Linaria vulgaris*, Toadflax

526. *Veronica spicata*, 'Spiked Speed-
     well'
527. *Veronica arvensis*, 'Wall Speedwell'
528. *Veronica persica*, 'Buxbaum's
     Speedwell'
529. *Veronica hederifolia*, 'Ivy Speedwell'

530. *Veronica alpina*, 'Alpine Speed-
     well'
531. *Veronica verna*, 'Spring Speedwell'
532. *Veronica agrestis*, 'Field Speed-
     well'

533. *Veronica chamaedrys,* 'Germander Speedwell'
534. *Veronica serpyllifolia,* 'Thyme-leaved Speedwell'
535. *Veronica beccabunga,* Brooklime
536. *Veronica officinalis,* 'Common Speedwell'
537. *Veronica scutellata,* 'Marsh Speedwell'

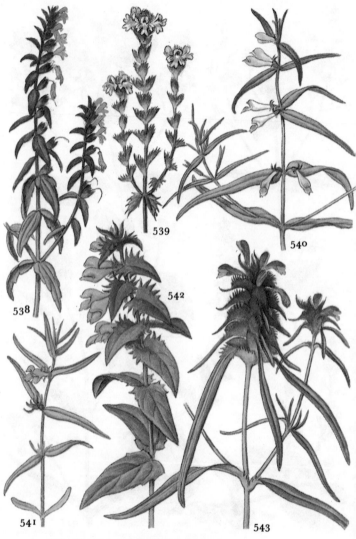

538. *Odontites rubra*, 'Red Bartsia'
539. *Euphrasia officinalis*, Eyebright
540. *Melampyrum pratense*, 'Common Cow-wheat'
541. *Melampyrum sylvaticum*, 'Wood Cow-wheat'
542. *Melampyrum nemorosum*, 'Forest Glade Cow-Wheat'
543. *Melampyrum cristatum*, 'Crested Cow-wheat'

544. *Rhinanthus serotinus*, 'Greater Yellow Rattle'
545. *Rhinanthus minor*, Yellow Rattle
546. *Bartsia alpina*, 'Alpine Bartsia'
547. *Pedicularis palustris*, Red-rattle
548. *Pedicularis sylvatica*, Lousewort

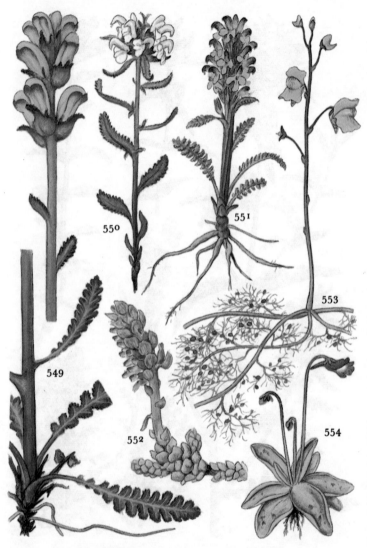

549. *Pedicularis sceptrum-carolinum*, 'Royal Sceptre Lousewort'
550. *Pedicularis lapponica*, 'Lapland Lousewort'
551. *Pedicularis oederi*, 'Oeder's Lousewort'
552. *Lathraea squamaria*, Toothwort
553. *Utriculica vulgaris*, 'Greater Bladderwort'
554. *Pinguicula vulgaris*, Common Butterwort

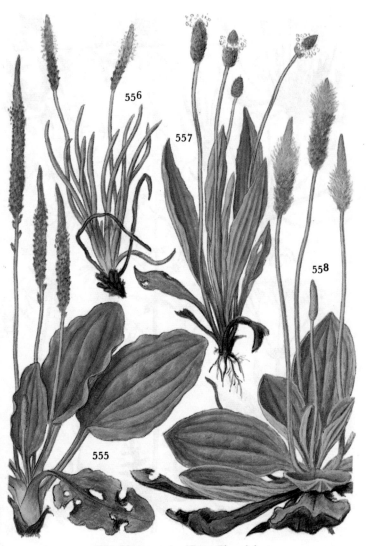

555. *Plantago major*, 'Great Plantain'
556. *Plantago maritima*, 'Sea Plantain'
557. *Plantago lanceolata*, Ribwort
558. *Plantago media*, 'Hoary Plantain'

559. *Plantago coronopsis*, Buck's-horn
Plantain
560. *Littorella uniflora*, Shore-weed
561. *Sherardia arvensis*, Field Madder
562. *Asperula odorata*, Sweet Woodruff

563. *Galium boreale*, 'Northern Bedstraw'
564. *Galium saxatile*, 'Heath Bedstraw'
565. *Galium palustre*, 'Marsh Bedstraw'

566. *Galium mollugo*, 'Great Hedge Bedstraw'
567. *Galium verum*, Lady's Bedstraw
568. *Galium aparine*, Cleavers
569. *Lonicera periclymenum*, Honeysuckle
570. *Lonicera xylosteum*, Fly Honeysuckle

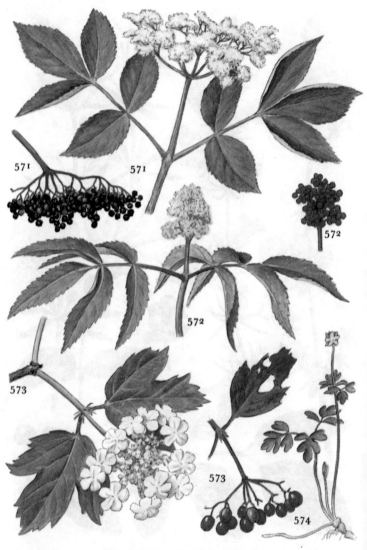

571. *Sambucus nigra*, Elder
572. *Sambucus racemosa*, 'Grape Elder'
573. *Viburnum opulus*, Guelder Rose
574. *Adoxa moschatellina*, Moschatel

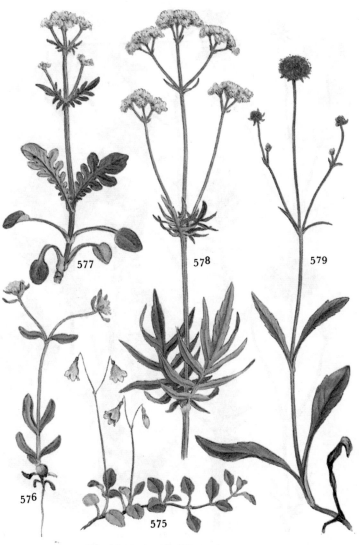

575. *Linnaea borealis*, 'Linnaea'
576. *Valerianella locusta*, Lamb's Lettuce
577. *Valeriana dioeca*, Marsh Valerian
578. *Valeriana sambucifolia*, Valerian
579. *Succisa pratensis*, Devil's-bit Scabious

580. *Scabiosa columbaria*, 'Small Scabious'
581. *Knautia arvensis*, Field Scabious
582. *Campanula persicifolia*, 'Narrow-leaved Campanula'
583. *Campanula latifolia*, 'Large Campanula'
584. *Campanula trachelium*, Bats-in-the-Belfrey

585. *Campanula rapunculoides,* 'Creeping Campanula'
586. *Campanula patula,* 'Spreading Campanula'
587. *Campanula glomerata,* 'Clustered Bellflower'
588. *Campanula rotundifolia,* Harebell, Bluebell of Scotland
589. *Jasione montana,* Sheep's Bit
590. *Lobelia dortmanna,* 'Water Lobelia'

591. *Eupatorium cannabinum*, Hemp Agrimony
592. *Aster tripolium*, 'Sea Aster'
593. *Solidago virgaurea*, Golden Rod
594. *Erigeron acris*, 'Blue Fleabane'
595. *Erigeron canadense*, 'Canadian Fleabane'

596. *Erigeron uniflorum*, 'Alpine Fleabane'
597. *Bellis perennis*, Daisy
598. *Filago minima*, 'Slender Cudweed'
599. *Filago arvensis*, 'Field Cudweed'

600. *Antennaria dioica*, 'Cat's-foot'
601. *Antennaria alpina*, 'Alpine Cat's-
foot'
602. *Gnaphalium uliginosum*, 'Marsh
Cudweed'

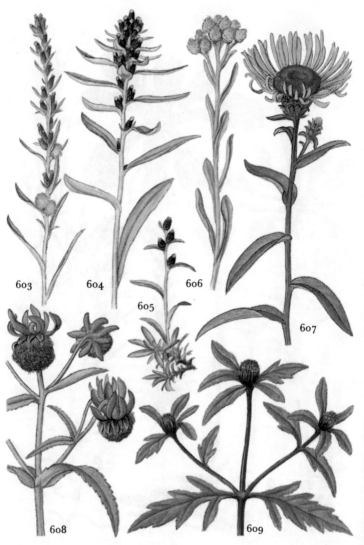

603. *Gnaphalium sylvaticum*, 'Wood Cudweed'

604. *Gnaphalium norvegicum*, 'Highland Cudweed'

605. *Gnaphalium supinum*, 'Dwarf Cudweed'

606. *Gnaphalium arenarium*, 'Sand Cudweed'

607. *Inula salicina*, 'Willow-leaved Inula'

608. *Bidens cernuus*, 'Nodding Bur-Marigold'

609. *Bidens tripartitus*, 'Tripartite Bur-Marigold'

610. *Galinsoga parviflora*, Gallant Soldier
611. *Anthemis arvensis*, Corn Chamomile
612. *Anthemis tinctoria*, Yellow Chamomile
613. *Achillea Ptarmica*, Sneezewort
614. *Achillea millefolium*, Yarrow
615. *Chrysanthemum segetum*, Corn Marigold

616. *Chrysanthemum leucanthemum*, Ox-eye Daisy
617. *Tanacetum vulgare*, Tansy
618. *Matricaria maritima*, 'Scentless Mayweed'
619. *Matricaria matricarioides*, 'Rayless Mayweed'
620. *Matricaria chamomilla*, Wild Chamomile
621. *Artemisia campestris*, 'Field Southernwood'

622. *Artemisia vulgaris*, Mugwort
623. *Artemisia maritima*, 'Sea Wormwood'
624. *Artemisia absinthium*, Wormwood
625. *Tussilago farfara*, Coltsfoot
626. *Petasites hybridus*, Butterbur

627. *Petasites frigidus*, 'Winter Butterbur'
628. *Senecio sylvaticus*, 'Wood Groundsel'
629. *Senecio vernalis*, 'Spring Senecio'
630. *Senecio viscosus*, 'Stinking Groundsel'
631. *Senecio vulgaris*, Groundsel

632. *Senecio jacobaea,* Ragwort
633. *Arnica montana,* 'Mountain Arnica'
634. *Arctium tomentosum,* 'Cottony Bur-
    dock'

635. *Arctium minus*, 'Lesser Burdock'
636. *Carlina vulgaris*, Carline Thistle
637. *Carduus crispus*, 'Welted Thistle'
638. *Cirsium acaule*, 'Stemless Thistle'

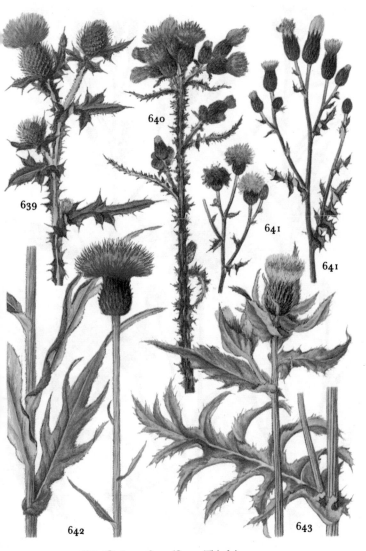

639. *Cirsium vulgare*, 'Spear Thistle'
640. *Cirsium palustre*, 'Marsh Thistle'
641. *Cirsium arvense*, Creeping Thistle
642. *Cirsium heterophyllum*, Melancholy Thistle
643. *Cirsium oleraceum*, 'Cabbage Thistle'

644. *Saussuria alpina,* 'Alpine Saussurea'
645. *Serratula tinctoria,* 'Saw-wort'
646. *Centaurea cyanus,* Cornflower
647. *Centaurea scabiosa,* 'Greater Knapweed'
648. *Centaurea jacea,* 'Brown-rayed Knapweed'

649. *Cichorium intybus*, Chichory
650. *Lapsana communis*, Nipplewort
651. *Lactuca muralis*, 'Wall Lettuce'
652. *Cicerbita alpina*, 'Blue Sow-thistle'

653. *Hypochoeris radicata*, 'Cat's Ear'
654. *Hypochoeris maculata*, 'Spotted Cat's Ear'
655. *Leontodon autumnalis*, 'Autumnal Hawkbit'
656. *Tragopodon pratensis*, Jack-go-to-bed-at-noon
657. *Scorzonera humilis*, 'Dwarf Scorzonera'

658. *Sonchus arvensis*, 'Field Milk-Thistle'
659. *Sonchus oleraceus*, Sow-Thistle
660. *Taraxacum vulgare*, Dandelion
661. *Crepis biennis*, 'Rough Hawk's-beard'
662. *Crepis praemorsa*, 'Bitten-off Hawk's-beard'

663. *Crepis tectorum,* 'Roof-tile Hawk's-beard'
664. *Crepis paludosa,* 'Marsh Hawk's-beard'
665. *Hieracium pilosella,* Mouse-ear Hawkweed
666. *Hieracium umbellatum,* Hawkweed
667. *Hieracium vulgatum,* 'Common Hawkweed'

PLANT DESCRIPTIONS

As mentioned in the Foreword, the intention of this book is to enable people to learn the names of the wild flowers to be found in nature, by comparing the plants with the illustrations in the colour plates.

The descriptions of the plants given on the following pages are intended only as a complement to the pictures and are therefore quite short; they merely stress the more obvious characteristics by means of which it is possible to recognise one plant species from another. Further information given is the size of each plant, its frequency, the localities where it is generally to be found and its time of flowering. If the plant in question is poisonous, this is also indicated.

The terms used in describing the plants should be understandable by anybody with no previous botanical knowledge, provided the descriptions are compared with the corresponding pictures on the colour plates; as a rule only those characteristics have been included which can be observed with the naked eye. In the case of the grasses, however, with their small, inconspicuous flowers, it has been necessary to include references to anatomical features best observed through a magnifying glass. We cannot stress too much, however, the advisability of using a magnifying glass also when looking at the flowers of other plants. In this way our eyes are opened to a world of beauty which would otherwise remain closed to us.

The plant descriptions have been numbered to correspond with the pictures in the colour plates. Some of the species in the text have an 'a' or a 'b' after their number. These plants are not illustrated in the colour plates, because they resemble so closely the picture of the plant whose number they bear that it has not been necessary to give them a picture of their own.

After becoming familiar with some of our wild plants through the pictures in this book, it might be profitable to consult a complete flora containing determination keys, with the aid of which the reader is led step by step towards finding the name of an unknown plant. A list of suitable books is given on p. 222.

---

1 Pinus sylvestris *Scot's Pine*

A tall tree with grey-green needle-like leaves in pairs. The cones are pendant and have short stalks. This tree is a native in the Highlands but probably introduced into England where it is grown extensively. Flowers May-June. On the colour plate, top left, a dense cluster of yellow male flowers is shown. Below is a branch with cones and with red female inflorescences at the tips of the new shoots.

1a Pinus mugo *Mountain Pine*

Resembles the above species but is usually a low, spreading shrub and can otherwise be recognised by its dark green needles and stemless cones. Not a native but planted for shelter in exposed places. Flowers May-June.

2 Picea abies *Norway Spruce*

A tall tree with the needles arranged singly on the branches. The cones are long and hanging. Not a native but sometimes planted. Flowers May-June.

3 Juniperus communis *Juniper*

A shrub or small tree with prickly, awl-shaped needles in whorls of three. Male and female flowers grow on different plants. Female flowers become fleshy when ripe (juniper berries). Common on chalk downs, on heaths and in pine or birch woods on poor soil. Flowers May-June.

At the bottom left of the illustration is shown a branch of a female plant with ripe fruits, and to the right of it there is a twig with yellow male flowers.

4 Taxus baccata *Yew*

A stout tree, up to 20 m. high with short, narrow leaves, dark above, paler below. Male and female flowers are borne on different plants. When ripe the seeds are surrounded by a juicy, red aril. Grows on chalky downs, heaths and moors. Flowers April-May.
This plant is poisonous.
The colour plate shows a branch with needles, bottom right. Above it to the left there is a shoot with yellow male flowers and to the right, a shoot with ripe seeds.

5 Typha latifolia *Cat's Tail*, 'Great Reedmace'

A bog plant, 1-2.5 m. (3-8 ft) high, with long, linear leaves, 1-2 centimeters (3/8-3/4 ft) wide. The unisexual flowers are arranged in a thick, cylindrical spike, the upper part consisting exclusively of male flowers and the lower part of female flowers. Common in lakes, ponds and slow-flowing rivers. Flowers in July.
The illustration shows a plant sketch-

ed in the autumn. The male part of the spike has withered, while the female part now consists of innumerable tiny fruits with downy hairs.

5a Typha angustifolia 'Lesser Reedmace'

Resembles the above species but can be recognised by its narrower leaves, only 0.5-1 cm (3/16-3/8 ins.), and by the male and the female parts of the spike being separated by a 3-5 cm (1 1/4-2 ins.) long bare piece of stem. Common on the margins of lakes and streams, especially where the water is fairly deep. Flowers in July.

6 Sparganium erectum *Bur-reed*

Bog plant, 30-90 cm (1-3 ft) tall, with stems branched at the top. The flowers are unisexual; male and female flowers are in separate, globular heads with the male at the top and the female at the base of the branches. Common in shallow water on the margins of lakes and in streams and ditches. Flowers July-August.

7 Sparganium simplex 'Unbranched Bur-reed'

Resembles *S. erectum* but is slightly smaller and the stem is not branched but the lower flower-heads may be stalked. Common in similar places. Flowers July-August.
The colour plate shows a plant bearing fruit.

8 Calla palustris

Bog plant, 15-30 cm (6-12 ins.) tall, with a horizontal, creeping or floating stem, heart-shaped leaves and small densely packed flowers at the base of which there is a snow-white spathe or enclosing leaf. Berries red. Introduced in 1861; grows in bogs and near ponds. Flowers June-July.

Arum maculatum
Lords-and-Ladies, Cuckoo-pint

Perennial plant with a tuberous rhizome from which long-stalked, arrow-shaped leaves arise in spring. The flower-spike is surrounded by a greenish spathe from which only the bare, violet-brown top of the spike appears. Berries red. Grows in woods and thickets on rich leaf-mould throughout England, Wales and Ireland; rarer in Scotland. Flowers May-June.

10 Acorus calamus *Sweet Flag*

Bog plant approximately 1 m (3 ft) high with narrow, transversely wavy leaves and small, yellowish-green flowers in an apparently lateral spike. Introduced in 1557; in shallow water at the edges of lakes, streams and ponds. Flowers June-July.

11 Lemna trisulca 'Ivy Duckweed'

The Duckweeds are small, floating water-plants with stems and leaves modified to form small, green fronds which multiply by side shoots. Most species have round fronds, but those of the Ivy Duckweed are oblong and stalked. Common on still waters Flowers June-July, but the inconspicuous, greenish flowers are rarely seen.

12 Lemna minor
Duckweed, Duck's-meat

The smallest flowering plant in our flora. It has circular or oval fronds, green on both sides, and one root only under each frond. Common in ponds and ditches where it forms green patches on the surface of the water, Flowers June-July.

13 Lemna polyrrhiza
'Great Duckweed'

Fronds comparatively large, red underneath, each with several roots. Not

very common. Flowers (extremely rarely) June-July.

14 Sagittaria sagittifolia
Arrow-head

Bog plant, 30-90 cm (1-3 ft) tall, with arrow-shaped leaves rising out of the water, and white flowers with reddish centres. Grows on the edges of lakes and streams; most frequent in southern England, otherwise rare. Flowers July-August.

15 Alisma plantago-aquatica
Water Plantain

Bog plant, 30-90 cm (1-3 ft) high, with long-stalked, ellipitical leaves. Flowers small, pale lilac in a branched inflorescence. Common on the edge of lakes, in ponds and ditches. Flowers June-August.

16 Butomus umbellatus
Flowering Rush

Beautiful bog plant, 90-150 cm high, with long, narrow leaves, triangular at the base, and large, pinkish red flowers in an umbel at the top. Fairly common on the edges of lakes and rivers; rather local. Flowers June-August.

17 Triglochin palustre
'Marsh Arrow Grass'

A slender plant, 15-40 cm (6-16 ins.) high, with grass-like leaves and a thin spike of small, greenish flowers. Fruit splitting (a schizocarp) with 3 narrow pointed carpels. Common on marshes among tall grass. Flowers June-July.

18 Triglochin maritimum
'Sea Arrow Grass'

A tuft-forming plant, 15-60 cm (6-24 ins.) high, with cylindrical, succulent leaves and a spike of small, greenish flowers. Fruit splitting (schizocarp) with 6 rounded carpels. Common on Salt Marshes in turf. Flowers June-August.

19 Scheuchzeria palustris
'Marsh Scheuchzeria'

A rush-like plant, 10-20 cm (4-8 ins.) high, with inconspicuous, yellowish-green flowers. The fruits, shown in the illustration, are more spectacular; they are compound fruits, consisting of 3-4 inflated carpels. Grows in sphagnum bogs but is rare except in the Highlands. Flowers June-July.

20 Potamogeton natans
'Broad-leaved Pondweed'

The Pondweed species are perennial water plants forming dense, submerged growths in lakes and streams. The tiny, green, 4-petaled flowers are held in dense spikes rising above the surface of the water. Common throughout the British Isles.

The Broad-leaved Pondweed has long-stalked, oval floating leaves on the surface of the water, and long, narrow submerged leaves. Common in running water as well as in lakes and ponds. Flowers June-July.

21 Potamogeton gramineus
'Various-leaved Pondweed'

Oval, long-stalked floating leaves and lanceolate, stemless, submerged leaves. Rather local throughout the British Isles, chiefly in lakes and streams. Flowers June-August.

22 Potamogeton perfoliatus
'Perfoliate Pondweed'

All the leaves of this plant are submerged, clasping the stems with their heart-shaped bases. Common throughout the British Isles; it also occurs in brackish water. Flowers June-August.

22a Potamogeton pectinatus
'Fennel-leaved Pondweed'

Much-branched water plant with stiff, bristly, submerged leaves. There are no floating leaves. Common in brackish water in ponds and ditches; also occurs in lakes and streams; absent in mountainous districts of Wales and Scotland. Flowers June-August.

23 Elodea canadensis
Canadian Pondweed

A submerged water plant, rooted at the base, with densely packed, oblong leaves in whorls of three. A native of North America but now fairly common in lakes and streams throughout the British Isles. The female plants are chiefly found here, male flowers are very rare. The female flowers are reddish-white with red stigmas and are carried on long stems to the surface of the water. Flowers July-September.

24 Hydrocharis morsus-ranae
Frog-bit

Water plant with heart-shaped, floating leaves and white flowers. Common in small lakes and ponds, usually in chalky districts.

25 Stratioites aloides
Water Soldier

A floating water plant with funnel-shaped rosettes of long, narrow, stiff leaves, with spiney edges resembling an Aloe; white, unisexual flowers. Female plants are chiefly found in the north, whilst in the south the male plants predominate. Flowers July-August.

26 Fritillaria meleagris
Fritillary, Snakes Head

A bulbous plant, stem 20-30 cm (8-12 ins.) high, with narrow leaves and a nodding flower chequered in darker and lighter red (seldom whitish). In moist meadows but very local, especially in the south. Grown in gardens. Flowers in May.

27 Allium ursinum *Ramsons*

A bulbous plant, 15-45 cm (6-18 ins.)

high, with 2 basal, elliptical leaves and a triangular stem bearing a flat umbel of white, star shaped flowers. Native, in damp woods. Flowers May-June.

28 Allium scorodoprasum
'Sand Leek'

A bulbous plant which grows 60-80 cm (24-32 ins.) high, with flat, narrow leaves and reddish purple flowers. Native but very local on dry soils on grassland or scrub. Flowers July-August.

29 Alium oleraceum 'Field Garlick'

Plant 50-60 cm (20-24 ins.) high, with hollow, linear leaves and long-stalked, pink flowers with darker stripes. There are purple bulbils between the few flowers and the inflorescence is sheathed in 2 bracts with long points. Native but rather local, on grassy downs and on roadsides. Flowers July-August.

29a Allium vineale Crow Garlick

Resembles the Field Garlick, but can easily be recognised by having, as a rule, a compact clump of bulbs only at the top of the stem instead of flowers. The 'inflorescence' is enveloped in a single spathe with short points. Grows in fields and on roadsides, common in England but rather local in Scotland. Flowers July-August.

30 Allium schoenoprasum Chives

A 10-30 cm (4-12 ins.) high plant with cylindrical, grass-like leaves forming clumps and with purple flowers in a densely packed umbel, without bulbils. Grown as a culinary herb; native but very local. Flowers June-July.

31 Gagea lutea
'Yellow Star-of-Bethlehem'

Bulbous plant, 10-30 cm (4-12 ins.) tall, with a single, long narrow basal leaf and 3-6 yellow flowers, greenish on the outside, in an umbel subtended by 2 green bracts. Grows in damp woods and dastures, very local. Flowers April-May.

32 Paris quadrifolia Herb Paris

A plant with stems 15-35 cm (6-14 ins.) high and 4 (more rarely 3-5) leaves in a whorl with a single, yellowish-green flower in the centre. The fruit is a purple-black berry. Rather local in damp woods. Flowers May-June. *This plant is poisonous.*

33 Tofieldia pusilla
'Scottish Asphodel'

Plant 5-20 cm (2-8 ins.) high, with narrow, radical leaves and a short dense head of small greenish white flowers. By streams and on mountains, local.

34 Narthecium ossifragum
Bog Asphodel

Plant 15-35 cm (6-14 ins.) high with radical, narrow, sword-shaped leaves and yellow flowers in a raceme. In bogs and wet places on mountains. Flowers July-August. *This plant is poisonous.*

35 Polygonatum verticillatum
'Whorled Solomon's Seal'

Plant 30-70 cm (12-28 ins.) high, with narrow leaves in whorls and 3-4 small, white flowers with green tips in the axils of the leaves. Very rare, in the north of the British Isles, in woods. Flowers May-June. *This plant is poisonous.*

36 Polygonatum odoratum
'Angular Solomon's Seal'

Plant 15-45 cm (6-18 ins.) high with angular, arching stem and ovate leaves in the axils of which the fragrant, fairly large, white flowers with green tips, are borne, singly or in pairs. The fruit is a blue-black berry. In limestone woods, very local. Flowers May-June. *This plant is poisonous.*

36a Polygonatum multiflorum
Solomon's Seal

Resembles the foregoing species, but differs in the round, smooth stem, 30-60 cm (1-2 ft) high and the slightly smaller flowers which are not scented, and are held 2-5 together in the axils of the leaves. Fairly common in woods in England and Wales, naturalised in Scotland. Flowers April-May. *This plant is poisonous.*

37 Convallaria majalis
Lily-of-the-Valley

Plant 15-25 cm (6-10 ins.), with elliptical, radical leaves and a one-sides raceme of fragrant, white, bell-shaped flowers. Berries red. Common in woods and thickets on calcareous soils in England, but more local in Wales and Scotland. Flowers May-June. *This plant is poisonous.*

38 Maianthemum bifolium
May Lily

Plant 5-15 cm (2-6 ins.) high with heart-shaped leaves and tiny, white, 4-petalled flowers in a terminal cluster. Berries at first spotted, then pure red. Doubtfully native, in woods, very rare.

39 Iris pseudacorus *Yellow Flag*

Robust marsh plant, 60-120 cm (2-4 ft) high, with long sword-shaped leaves arising from a rhizome, and large yellow flowers. Common on the edge of ponds, streams and in marshes. Flowers June-July.

40 Juncus articulatus
'Jointed Rush'

Very variable in size and habit; stem prostrate or erect, about 15-40 cm (6-16 ins.) long, laterally compressed, curved with transverse cross partitions on the inner side. Flowers in terminal clusters on a much branched stem. Like the other rushes, the flowers have 6 membraneous perianth leaves. Very common on wet, acid soil in and near water. Flowers July-August.

41 Juncus conglomeratus
'Compact Rush'

This plant has cylindrical, finely ridged, dull green stems and leaves 50-80 cm (20-32 ins.) high in dense tufts. The leaves are cylindrical resembling the stems. The flowers are in a lateral, globular, compact inflorescence. Common in damp places on acid soils.

42 Juncus effusus *Soft Rush*

Resembles the previous species but can be recognised by its glossy green, almost smooth stems and leaves, and a looser and more spreading flower panicle. Common in similar places. Flowers June-July.

43 Juncus bufonius *Toad Rush*

A small annual plant with 3-25 cm (1-10 ins.) high, thread-like, branched stems and whitish-green flowers. Common on wet ground. Flowers June-August.

44 Luzula pilosa *'Hairy Woodrush'*

Plant 10-25 cm (4-10 ins.) high with stems in tufts and grass-like leaves covered with long, white hairs. The flowers are single, rarely in pairs, on thin stalks in a terminal, umbel-like inflorescence. Common in woods and hedges. Flowers April-May.

45 Luzula campestris *Sweep's Brush, 'Field Woodrush'*

A plant 5-20 cm (2-8 ins.) high with hairy leaves and flowers in spherical clusters, finally drooping. Common on open, grassy ground. Flowers March-May.

46 Sesleria caerulea *'Blue Sesleria'*

A grass 15-50 cm (6-20 ins.) tall, the stems tufted and ending in a bluish-violet, spike-like tassel. Grows on chalky hills and pastures, chiefly in northern England and western Ireland. Flowers May-June.

47 Molinia caerulea
'*Purple Moor-grass*'

Has stiff erect stems, 50-120 cm (20-48 ins.) high, in compact tufts. The leaves have a fringe of hairs instead of a ligule. The small 2-4-flowered spikelets are carried on a long, greenish-purple stem with thin branches. Common on damp soil, in marshes heaths and fens. Flowers July-August.

48 Nardus stricta *Mat-grass*

Grows in compact tufts with stiff leaves and stems 15-30 cm (6-12 ins.), ending in narrow spikes with one-sided, one-flowered spikelets. Common on poor, sandy soil on moors and mountains. Flowers June-July.

49 Phragmites communis *Reed*

Our tallest reed; it has stems 1-3 m (3-10 ft) high and broad leaves with a fringe of hairs instead of the ligule. The inflorescence is a large, loose panicle composed of dark purple 4-6-flowered spikelets with long silky hairs between the flowers. Common on wet ground; forms a dense swamp of reeds at the edges of fresh water and even on the seashore in brackish water. Flowers August-September.

50 Melica uniflora *Wood Melick*

A slender grass 30-45 cm (12-18 ins.) tall, with drooping leaves and a more or less one-sided spike with few flowers in erect spikelets which consist of one bisexual and one sterile flower in each. Common on leaf-mould in light beech-woods. Flowers May-June.

51 Melica nutans '*Mountain Melick*'

Like the previous plant but with a narrow spike consisting of short-stalked, one-sided, nodding spikelets containing two fertile and one sterile flower. Grows in shady woods and hedges. Flowers May-June.

52 Glyceria fluitans *Flote-grass*

An aquatic grass with 0.5-1 m (20-40 ins.) long, floating or erect stems and a long, sparingly branched inflorescence with long, narrow, 7-13-flowered spikelets. Common on the edges of ponds and ditches. Flowers June-July.

53 Glyceria maxima *Reed Grass*

A swamp grass, 1-2 m (3-6 ft) tall, with erect stems and broad basal leaves, the latter with a jutting keel. The inflorescence is very large and many-flowered with comparatively short spikelets. Common on the margins of lakes and streams. Flowers July-August.

54 Phalaris arundinacea *Reed Grass*

A robust grass with stems 1-2 m (3-6 ft) high, bearing broad leaves that end in large, lobed, pale green or purplish panicles, the flower stems forming a compact spike. The spikelets are one-flowered. Common in wet soil, on the margins of lakes and rivers. Flowers June-July.

55 Festuca pratensis
'*Meadow Fescue*'

A loosely tufted grass with 30-60 cm (12-24 ins.) high stems, flat smooth leaves and a somewhat one-sided, slightly nodding flower stem with narrow, 5-10-flowered spikelets without awns. Common in meadows, on roadsides and pastures; valuable for grazing and as hay. Flowers June-August.

55a Festuca gigantea '*Tall Brome*'

More robust than *F. pratensis,* the stems more than 3 ft high with dark-brown nodes and broad, drooping, glossy, dark-green leaves. The flower stem has long, narrow branches and the spikelets are equiped with long, waving awns. Common in woods and hedges. Flowers July-September.

56 Festuca rubra
'Creeping Fescue'

Has 25-60 (10-24 ins.) high, scattered culms ending in a reddish, more or less one-sided flower spike consisting of 4-7-flowered, awn-bearing spikelets. The radical leaves have red sheaths and bristle-shaped, infolded blades; the stem leaves are flat. Common everywhere on grassland. Flowers June-August.

The colour plate shows on the left a stem with the top branches contracted after flowering, and on the right a spike with spreading branches sketched during the flowering period.

57 Festuca ovina *Sheep's Fescue*

Forms dense tussocks with thread-like leaves and slender, 10-20 cm (4-12 ins.) long stems ending in a short-branched, stiffly erect spike with few flowers in the short-awned spikelets. Common on dry downs and heaths. Flowers May-June.

58 Poa pratensis *Meadow-grass*

A perennial, 10-80 cm (1-32 ins.) tall which has a loose spike with ovate, 3-5-flowered, compressed, awnless spikelets. The stems and leaf-sheaths are smooth and the ligule is truncated. Common on meadows, commons and roadsides. A native but cultivated for grazing and for hay. Flowers May-June.

58a Poa trivialis
Rough Meadow-grass

Resembles the previous plant, but differs in having rough stems and leaf-

sheaths and a long, pointed ligule. Common in meadows, ditches and forest bogs. Flowers June-July.

59 Poa annua *'Annual Poa'*

A small, annual, tufted grass with flattened stems 5-20 cm (2-8 ins.) long, and cross-crinkled leaves. The topmost branches spread out during flowering but droop later. Native but a common weed on cultivated soil; also grows along roads and forest paths. Flowers throughout the year.

60 Poa nemoralis *Wood Poa*

Perennial grass with slender stems, 30-80 cm (12-32 ins.) high, in loose tufts. The nodes are brown and the leaves at right angles to the stem. The spike is nodding with hair-like branches. Common in dry places in woods and thickets. Flowers July-August.

61 Dactylis glomerata *Cock's-foot*

A tussock-forming grass with stout, 0.5-1 m (19-38 ins.) high stems ending in a lop-sided, pyramidal spike with densely packed, 2-5-flowered spikelets at the ends of the top branches. Common in fields, along roads and in woods; cultivated for grazing and hay. Flowers June-July.

62 Briza media
Quaking Grass, Doddering Dillies

A tufted grass, 15-45 cm (6-18 ins.) high. Easily recognised by its many-coloured, heart-shaped, multi-flowered spikelets, hanging from the tips of spreading, hair-like branches. Fairly common in meadows and on grassy slopes. Flowers June-July.

63 Cynosurus cristatus
'Crested Dog's-tail'

A tussock-forming grass with wiry stems, 20-50 cm (8-20 ins.) high ending in a narrow, spike-like cluster consisting of two rows of one-sided, multi-flowered spikelets, each surrounded by a comb-shaped, lobed bract or glume (a sterile spikelet). Common in meadows and pastures. Flowers June-July.

64 Avena pubescens '*Hairy Oat*'

A loosely tufted grass with soft, hairy leaves and stems 30-60 cm (1-2 ft) high, ending in a spike with erect, 2-3 flowered, silvery purplish, long-awned spikelets. Fairly common in meadows and pastures and on roadsides. Flowers May June.

64a Avena pratensis '*Meadow Oat*'

Resembles the plant above but differs in its dense tuft of small, stiff, smooth, bluish-green leaves and its narrower spike of somewhat larger (4-5 flowered) spikelets. Fairly common on chalky slopes and pastures. Flowers June-July.

65 Avena elatior
Tall or False Oat-grass

A tussock forming grass with stems 60-120 cm (2-4 ft.) high and a long, fairly narrow spike. The spikelets are two-flowered; the lowest flower is male and awned, the upper is bisexual and, as a rule, awnless. Very common in rough, grassy places. Flowers June-July.

65a Avena fatua *Wild Oat*

A stubborn weed in spring crops (barley and oats). It resembles cultivated oats, but is smaller and easily recognised by its hairy, long-awned grains which fall out of the spikelets on ripening. Introduced and now naturalised in England and Scotland. Flowers June to August.

66 Deschampsia caespitosa
Tufted Hair-grass

A 0.5-1 m (19-38 ins.) tall grass with a large, dense tuft of long, narrow, ribbed, rough leaves and with a large open spike of silvery purplish, 2-flowered spikelets with short awns. Common in meadows and wet woods. Flowers June-July.

67 Deschampsia flexuosa
Wavy Hair-grass

Tufted grass with soft, bristle-shaped leaves, 30-50 cm (12-20 ins.) high stems and a spreading panicle with silky, brownish-purple spikelets on hair-like, wavy, flexuous branches. Common on heaths and in woods on acid soils. Flowers June-July.

68 Holcus lanatus *Yorkshire Fog*

A 20-60 cm (8-24 ins.) tall, greyish, velvety-haired grass with a spike which is reddish on one side, greenish-white on the other. The spikelets are 2-flowered: the lower floret is bisexual and awnless; the upper is male with a short awn. Common in waste places fields, on roadsides and in woods. Flowers June-July.

68a Holcus mollis
'*Creeping Soft-grass*'

Differs from the above species by being almost smooth (only the nodes of the stems and the leaf-sheaths are hairy), and by having a pale yellowish brown spikelet and a longer awn. Fairly common on poor soil in waste places and open woods. Flowers July-August.

69 Bromus mollis *Lop-grass*

A soft, downy haired, 15-70 cm (6-27 ins.) high grass with an erect spike and oval, awn-bearing, 5-9-flowered spikelets. Common in meadows, on roadsides and dunes. Flowers June-July.

70 Ammophila arenaria
Marram Grass

A tall grass 0.5-1 m (19-38 ins.) high

with pale bluish-grey, inrolled stiff, prickly leaves and a densely compressed spike of 1-flowered spikelets. Common on dunes. Flowers July-August.

71 Elymus arenarius *Lyme Grass*

A robust, bluish-grey grass, the stems 90-120 cm (3-4 ft) high; leaves fairly broad, stiff and prickly and a stout, compound spike with 3-4 flowered spikelets, in pairs at each node of the spike. Common on sandy shores. Flowers June-August.

72 Calamagrostis epigejos
'Bush Grass'

A tall grass up to 0.7-1.5 m (28 ins.-5 ft) with stiff, rough stems and a large lobed, brownish-purple spike, consisting of one-flowered spikelets with long hairs at the base of the flowers. The leaves have a long ligule. In damp woods, ditches and fens. Flowers July-August.

73 Calamagrostis canescens
'Purple Smallreed'

Stems 0.7-1.2 m (28 ins.-4 ft) high, branched at the base, and a soft, loose, reddish-brown spike. The leaves have a short ligule. Common in fens and wet meadows. Flowers June-August.

74 Agrostis tenuis
'Common Bent Grass'

Has tufted stems 10-50 cm (4-20 ins.) high and a many-flowered, open, loose spike consisting of tiny, 1-flowered spikelets on hair-like branches. The leaves have a short ligule. Common on dry, acid soil. Flowers June-August.

74a Agrostis stolonifera
'Creeping Bent'

Resembles *A. tenuis,* but differs in having its long, creeping stems (stolons), a long ligule and a spike which is contracted after flowering.

Common in damp places, in slightly salt, coastal marshes as well as on inland fresh-water meadows. Flowers July-August.

75 Milium effusum *'Wood Millet'*

An erect grass, 0.6-1.2 m (2-4 ft) high with broad, lax leaves and a large, loose, open spike consisting of 1-flowered spikelets on thin, spreading, finally drooping branches. Common in damp woods. Flowers in June.

76 Alopecurus pratensis
'Meadow Foxtail'

A 45-90 cm (18-36 ins.) high grass with erect, smooth stems, slightly round leaves and a soft, compact panicle. The spikelets are 1-flowered and have long-haired external glumes with a thin awn sticking out between them. Common in meadows and ditches, also grown for grazing and as hay. Flowers May-August.

77 Alopecurus geniculatus
Marsh Foxtail

Has 15-40 cm (6-16 ins.) long, jointed stems, prostrate and rooting at the base. The leaf-sheaths are inflated. The panicle is narrow and tinged with purple. Common in wet meadows and on the edges of ditches and ponds. Flowers June-August.

78 Phleum pratense *Timothy*

A grey-green grass with erect stems 40-90 cm (16-35 ins.) high and a stiff, cylindrical panicle. The spikelets are 1-flowered and compressed, the outer glumes ending in a rigid bristle. Cultivated for grazing and hay under the name of 'Timothy', and also common in the wild, in meadows and roadsides. Flowers June-September.

78a Phleum nodosum *Cat's-tail*

Resembles *P. pratense* but is smaller and

shorter. The 10-50 cm (4-20 ins.) high stems are swollen like bulbs at the base. The panicle is shorter and narrower, (only 3-6 mm (1/8-1/4 ins.) wide. Common on dry, grassy downs. Flowers June-September.

79 Phleum commutatum
'*Alpine Cats-tail*'

A 20-30 cm (8-12 ins.) high grass with a short, brownish-purple panicle. Native; in damp places on the higher mountains in England and Scotland. Flowers June-September.

80 Anthoxanthum odoratum
'*Sweet Vernal Grass*'

Has slender stems, 15-45 cm (6-18 ins.), and an oblong, sparsely flowered panicle, turning bright yellow when ripe. The spikelets are 3-flowered; the central floret is fertile and without an awn; the 2 lateral florets are barren and awned. Common in meadows as well as on heaths and moors. Flowers May-June.

81 Lolium perenne
Rye Grass, Ray Grass

A tuft-forming grass with smooth, glossy leaves and stems 20-60 cm (8-24 ins.) high. The spike consists of 8-10-flowered spikelets on opposite sides of the axis, their edges turning in towards the stem. Common in waste places and roadsides; also cultivated for grazing and for hay, and as a lawn grass. Flowers June-August.

82 Agropyron repens
Couch Grass, Scutch, Twitch

Has stems 30-120 cm (1-4 ft) high, which have hairy, rough leaves and a narrow spike with compact, 3-6 flowered spikelets, the broader side pressed against the stem. Common weed on cultivated land; also occurs in fields and waste places. Flowers June-August.

83 Hierochloe odorata *Holy Grass*

A 30-70 cm (12-18 ins.) tall grass with a loose spike of brown, shining spikelets. Grows in wet meadows, chiefly in Scotland and Ireland. Flowers April and May.

84 Hordeum murinum
'*Wall Barley*'

A tuft-forming grass with stems 10-30 cm (4-12 ins.) high, inflated leaf-sheaths and dense, pale green spikes, the spikelets—1-flowered and with a long rough awn on the outer glumes. Fairly common around towns. Flowers June-July.

85 Eriophorum vaginatum
Hare's Tail

A tuft-forming sedge with bristle-shaped basal leaves and 10-40 cm (4-16 ins.) high stems, the leaves without blades, and ending in a single spike of tiny, bisexual flowers. When the fruits ripen, the spikelets turn into large white, cottony tufts as the bristles change into cottony hairs. Grows in heath and mountain bogs, chiefly in the north, decreasing in the south. Flowers in April.

On the left of the colour plate is shown a flowering plant and on the right, a stem with ripe fruits.

86 Eriophorum angustifolium
'*Common Cotton Grass*'

Stems 20-60 cm (8-24 ins.) high bearing narrow leaves and ending in several spikelets on thin, smooth stalks. Common in fens and bogs and on wet moorland. Flowers April-May.

On the colour plate is shown the stem of a fruit-bearing plant.

87 Scirpus lacustris *Bulrush*

A bog plant with stout, spongy, leafless stems which may grow to a height of 2-3 m (6-12 ft), ending in a branched spike of small, reddish-brown, cone-like spikelets with tiny, bisexual flowers. Common in lakes and rivers. Flowers in June-July.

88 Scirpus maritimus
'*Sea Club-rush*'

Sedge 30-100 cm (12-40 ins.) high with sharply triangula stems bearing long, narrow leaves and ending in a close cluster of brown spikelets. Common in salt marshes. Flowers July-August.

89 Scirpus sylvaticus
'*Wood Club-rush*'

A 50-80 cm (20-32 ins.) high sedge with sharply triangular stems, long broad leaves and a much branched spike of small green spikelets. Fairly common in marshes and in woodland bogs. Flowers June-July.

90 Eleocharis palustris
'*Common Spike-rush*'

A 10-50 cm (4-20 ins.) high sedge with leafless, rush-like stems, each ending in a small, brown spike. Common in wet meadows and in shallow water on the margins of lakes and streams. Flowers June-August.

91 Rhynchospora alba
'*White Beak-sedge*'

A slender sedge, 20-30 cm (8-12 ins.) high, tuft-forming, with hairlike leaves and sparsely-flowered, whitish-yellow spikelets in clusters at the tips of the branches of the stem. Grows in mountain and heath bogs. Flowers June-July.

92 Carex arenaria '*Sand Sedge*'

A 15-40 cm (6-16 ins.) high sedge with creeping stems many feet long and the erect stems ending in a yellowish-brown, crowded spike. The flowers are unisexual as in other sedges, but in this species (and in No. 96) the male and

female flowers are in the same spikelet while in the other species illustrated, the 2 kinds of flower are in distinct spikelets. Common on dunes, heaths and uncultivated ground. Flowers June-July.

(There are over 70 species of *Carex* in the British Isles; only a few of the more easily recognised are mentioned here).

93 Carex nigra '*Common Sedge*'

Has 10-40 cm (4-16 ins.) long stems bearing yellowish-brown spikelets with male flowers at their tips and 2-3 erect, cylindrical, greenish-black female spikelets lower down. Common in bogs and beside water in acid soils. Flowers May-June.

94 Carex acuta '*Tufted Sedge*'

Has robust shoots up to 60-100 cm (24-40 ins.) high, with 2-3 compact erect male spikelets at the top, and 2-5 long, nodding female spikelets below. Fairly common in wet meadows and on the margins of rivers. Flowers in June.

95 Carex panacea *Carnation Grass*

Has 10-30 cm (4-12 ins.) high, greyish-green shoots with a single male spikelet at the top, and 1-3 brown and green, variegated, few-flowered female spikelets. Common in bogs and wet meadows. Flowers May-June.

96 Carex curta '*White Sedge*'

A tuft-forming sedge with 25-50 cm (10-20 ins.) long, grey-green shoots ending in a compound, spike-like inflorescence, consisting of ovate whitish-grey spikelets. Common in bogs and wet meadows, never on chalky soils. Flowers June-July.

97 Carex digitata '*Fingered Sedge*'

C. digitata has a dense rosette of grass-like basal leaves and slender, leafless stems, 10-25 cm (4-10 ins.) high, which have purple sheaths at their base and bear a single, small male spikelet and 2-3 thin, few-flowered female spikelets at their tip, the female spikelets extending beyond the male. Grows on wet marshes and by mountain streams in the highlands. Flowers May-June.

98 Carex pilulifera
'Pill-headed Sedge'

Grows in dense tufts and has thin, 20-35 cm (8-14 ins.) high stems bearing a single male spikelet at their tips, surrounded by 2-3 almost globular, greyish-green female spikelets. When ripe, the stems droop. Common in grassy places in woods and on hilly heaths. Flowers June-July.

99 Carex caryophyllea
'Spring Sedge'

Has creeping stems and 5-20 cm (2-8 ins.) high, erect shoots ending in a single male spikelet and 2-3 oblong, brownish-green female spikelets. Common on dry downs, especially if chalky, and on roadsides. Flowers in April.

100 Carex rostrata
'Beaked Sedge', 'Bottle Sedge'

Stems are 40-80 cm (16-32 ins.) high, bearing narrow, angled, greyish-green leaves. There are 1-3 male spikelets at the top of the stem and further down 2-4 erect, cylindrical female spikelets with compact, globular fruits which have pointed, projecting beaks. In fens and bogs with a constantly high water level, local. Flowers in June.

101 Cypripedium calceolus
Lady's Slipper

Orchid, 15-40 cm (6-16 ins.), with broad, sheathing leaves and a large terminal, reddish-brown flower with a yellow, slipper-shaped lip. Grows in woods on limestone; extremely rare, but local in Yorkshire and Durham.

102 Ophrys insectifera *Fly Orchid*

A 20-30 cm (8-12 ins.) high plant with oblong leaves and purplish-brown fly-like flowers in a long, few-flowered spike. Grows on limestone or chalk; not common but chiefly in England from S. Devon to West-moreland and Durham. Flowers in June.

103 Gymnadenia conopsea
Fragrant Orchid

A plant 20-40 cm (8-16 ins.) high with palmate tubers, narrow leaves and a long, many-flowered spike of small, sweet-scented, reddish-mauve flowers with a very slender spur. Grows in wet meadows, especially on limestone; locally abundant. Flowers June-July.

104 Orchis sambucina
'Elder Orchid'

A 10-25 cm (4-10 ins.) high plant with stout tubers, lobed at the tip, tongue-shaped leaves and a short spike of red and whitish-yellow flowers with a darker red-spotted lip. The flowers have a faint scent of elder and, like all the other *Orchis* species, have a fairly thick spur. Grows on uncultivated grassy slopes and in thickets. Not a native of the British Isles. Flowers May to June.

105 Orchis mascula
Early Purple Orchis

A 20-35 cm (8-14 ins.) high plant with oval tubers, entire leaves spotted brown or plain green, and a long loose spike of scarlet flowers. Fairly common in woods, copses or meadows. Flowers May-June.

106 Orchis militaris
'Soldier Orchis'

A 20-45 cm (8-18 ins.) tall plant with entire, ovoid tubers, broad eliptical leaves and a densely flowered spike of large, reddish-grey flowers with a deeply lobed, carmine lip. The plant grows on chalk on banks and edges of woods, rare. Flowers May-June.

106a Orchis purpurea *Lady Orchis*

Closely resembles the above plant but differs in having scarlet flowers, the lip whitish with red spots. Grows on limestone in light, open woods, rarely in open grassland. Confined to the southern counties of England. Flowers May-June.

107 Orchis strictifolia
Meadow Orchis

A 15-40 cm (6-16 ins.) high plant with deeply palmate tubers, a hollow stem and fairly narrow, generally unspotted leaves, broadest below the centre and with a sheathing tip. The flesh-coloured, red or more rarely whitish yellow flowers are comparatively small and held in dense, oblong spikes. Fairly common in bogs and wet meadows. Flowers in June.

107a Orchis latifolia *Marsh Orchis*

Resembles the previous species and has a similar hollow stem but differs in having broader, generally brown-spotted leaves with a flat tip and slightly larger, lilac-red flowers with a spotted and toothed lip. Fairly common in similar places. Flowers May to June.

108 Orchis maculata *Spotted Orchid*

A 15-60 cm (6-24 ins.) high plant with deeply palmate tubers. Stem hollow or filled with pith and fairly narrow, brown-spotted leaves. The flowers are a pale reddish-purple with dark red spots and stripes on the lip; they are held in a dense, cone-shaped spike. Common throughout southern England in fens and meadows, rarer in woods. Flowers June-July.

109 Platanthera bifolia
Lesser Butterfly Orchis

A 25-40 cm (10-16 ins.) high plant with 2 large, oval leaves at the base of the stem; the upper leaves are small and narrow. The flowers which are held in a narrow spike are white and sweet-scented and have a thin spur, 1.5 2 cm (5/8-3/4 ins.) long, with a hair-like tip. Grows on hilly pastures and in meadows, chiefly on calcareous soils. Flowers June-August.

109a Platanthera chlorantha
Greater Butterfly Orchid

Resembles the previous plant closely but differs by having larger, greenish-white flowers with a spur up to 3 cm (1-1¼ ins.), with a flattened, club-shaped point. Grows throughout the British Isles in open woods and on grassy hillsides. Flowers July-August.

110 Epipactis helleborine

A 25-60 cm (10-24 ins.) tall plant with leaves which are ovate at the base, becoming narrower towards the tip, and a long, slightly one-sided raceme of spurless flowers, greenish on the outside and brownish or reddish purple inside. Fairly common in woods and hedge rows, local. Flowers July-August.

111 Epipactus palustris
'*Marsh Helleborine*'

A 15-30 cm (6-20 ins.) high plant, with a creeping rhizome, lanceolate leaves and a one-sided raceme of compara-tively large flowers, the colour varying between white and reddish-brown. Locally frequent in fens and wet mead-ows. Flowers in July.

112 Corallorrhiza trifida *Coral-root*

A 10-20 cm (4-8 ins.) high plant with a coral-like, branching rootstock and small greenish flowers tinged with red at the tip. The stem has greenish-brown sheathing scales and no real leaves. Grows on damp ground in woods, on damp heaths and dunes from Westmorland to Ross and Inverness. Flowers May-June.

113 Listera ovata *Twayblade*

A 30-50 cm (12-20 ins.) high plant with 2 large, ovate leaves and a long thin spike of greenish flowers with narrow, 2-lobed lips. Common and locally abundant in moist woods and pastures. Flowers May-June.

114 Listera cordata
Lesser Twayblade

A slender, 6-15 cm (2-6 ins.) high plant with 2 heart-shaped leaves and a short spike of small brownish-green flowers. In mountain woods and peat moors chiefly in the north, very rare in the south-west. Flowers May-June.

115 Goodyera repens
'Creeping Lady's Tresses'

Rhizome creeping, stems erect, 10-20 cm (4-8 ins.) high, bearing ovate net-veined leaves at the base and ending in a one-sided spike of small whitish flowers. Local in pine woods, chiefly in the northern counties. Flowers July-August.

116 Neottia nidus-avis
Bird's-nest Orchid

A plant 20-30 cm (8-12 ins.) high with short, creeping rhizomes and densely packed, thick roots. There are no leaves since the plant is a saprophyte but the stem is covered with brown, sheathing scales and ends in a loose spike of brown flowers. Grows in shady woods especially of beech. Flowers June-July.

117 Populus tremula *Aspen*

A tree of medium height which has almost circular leaves, toothed at the edges, with a long, laterally compressed stalk which makes the leaves tremble in the wind. The flowers are unisexual, in hanging catkins with lobed scales, the male and female catkins on different plants. The seeds have a tuft of silky hairs and are distributed by the wind. Common in woods and thickets, especially on poor soils; chiefly in the north and west, rather local in the south and west of the British Isles. Flowers March-April.
To the left on the colour plate there is a branch of a female plant with leaves and ripe fruits; to the right, flowering male catkins.

118 Salix pentandra *Bay Willow*

A shrub or small tree with glossy, dark green leaves. The naked, unisexual flowers in catkins with entire scales (male and female on different plants). The male flowers of most willows have only 2 stamens, but the Bay Willow is distinguished by its 5 (-10) stamens in each male flower. Native in marshes and fens and wet woods from N. Wales, Yorkshire, to Sutherland; planted elsewhere. Flowers May to June, later than the leaves.

119 Salix caprea
Great Sallow, Goat Willow

A shrub or small tree with smooth, greyish-brown branches and broadly oval leaves, glabrous above and woolly underneath. Common in woods and hedges throughout the British Isles. Flowers in April, before the leaves.
The colour plate shows a branch in leaf; below to the left is a male catkin and to the right, a female one.

120 Salix cinerea *Common Sallow*

A 2-4 m (6-13 ft) high bush with grey downy twigs and crinkled, densely hairy leaves. Very local, in fens. Flowers April-May, before the leaves.

121 Salix aurita *'Eared Sallow'*

A 1-2 m (6-13 ft) high shrub with smooth, reddish twigs and inversely ovate leaves with short, turned-back points. Common in fens and forest bogs and on moist heaths. Flowers April-May, before the leaves.

122 Salix lapponum *'Downy Willow'*

Shrub about 1 m (3 ft) high, with smooth twigs and elliptical leaves with recurved edges and covered with grey down. Flowers in May. Rather local on wet rocks, chiefly in Westmoreland and Scotland.

123 Salix repens *'Creeping Willow'*

A very low shrub, 5-50 cm (2-20 ins.) high, with a creeping, underground stem, the stems being prostrate or erect, bearing small, lanceolate leaves with silky hairs on both sides. In fens and on heaths and dry, sandy ground throughout the British Isles, but local. Flowers April-May (a little earlier or at the same time as the leaves)

At the top of the colour plate can be seen a leaf-bearing twig and below, one with male catkins.

123a Salix arenaria
'Downy Mountain Willow'

Closely resembles the previous species, but can be recognised by its broader leaves which have silvery grey, silky hairs on both sides. Common on dunes and heaths. Flowers April-May.

124 Salix herbacea *'Least Willow'*

A dwarf shrub, 2-5 cm (¾-2 ins.) high with underground rhizomes and few aerial branches; the leaves are almost circular. Common on rock ledges on the higher mountains in the British Isles. Flowers June-August.

On the left of the colour plate can be seen a female plant with fruit, on the right, a flowering male plant.

125 Salix reticulata
'Reticulate Willow'

A 2-8 cm (¾-3 ins.) high, dwarf shrub with leathery leaves with a network of prominent veins. On rock ledges on high mountains, very local. Flowers June-July.

A flowering female plant can be seen on the colour plate.

126 Myrica gale
Bog Myrtle, Sweet Gale

A deciduous shrub, 30-90 cm (1-3 ft) high with very fragrant wedge-shaped leaves, toothed near the tip, and with unisexual flowers in short erect catkins (male and female catkins on different plants). Grows in bogs and fens throughout the British Isles. Flowers April-May, before the leaves.

127 Alnus glutinosa *Alder*

A tree of medium height, up to about 20 m (65 ft), with roundish, smooth leaves, slightly sticky when young. The male catkins are pendant; the female catkins resemble small cones when ripe. Common in fens and wet woods. Flowers March-April, before the leaves. The colour plate shows, on the far left, a twig with flowering male and female catkins; next to it there are ripe female catkins and on the far right, a twig with leaves and unripe fruits.

128 Alnus incana *'Grey Alder'*

A small tree with ovate, pointed, serrated leaves, green above, grey beneath. The female catkins have no stalks. Introduced; sometimes planted for shelter and becoming naturalised. Flowers February-March (before the leaves).

129 Betula verrucosa *'Silver Birch'*

A tall tree, up to 25 m (75 feet), with beautiful, white bark peeling off in thin flakes, and slender, pendulous branches.

The young twigs are a glossy reddish brown and their bark is uneven, with small resinous warts but no hairs. The leaves taper to a point and have sharply serrated edges. Common in England, rare in Scotland, on light soil in woods. Flowers April-May (at the same time as the leaves appear).

129a Betula pubescens *Birch*
Resembles the previous tree but differs in having downy twigs without resinous warts and with rounder leaves. Native; common in woods and bogs. Flowers April-May.

130 Betula nana '*Dwarf Birch*'
A low shrub with small, roundly toothed leaves and short, erect catkins. Native but very local on high moorlands in the north. Flowers May-June.

131 Corylus avellana *Hazel, Cob-nut*
A large, many-stemmed shrub with roundish, saw-toothed leaves. The nuts are entirely enveloped in the lobed husks. Common in woods and thickets. Flowers March-April, before the leaves. The colour plate shows, at the top, a twig with leaves and fruits and below, a flowering twig with yellow, drooping male catkins and buds of female flowers with their red stigmas protruding.

132 Carpinus betulus *Hornbeam*
A medium sized tree with oval, pointed serrate leaves. The fruit is a compressed nut with a one-sided, 3-lobed husk. Common in woods and hedgerows; native in England, planted elsewhere in the British Isles. Flowers in May. On the left of the colour plate can be seen a twig with leaves and fruits, on the right a flowering twig with a female catkin at the top and two male catkins to the right of the leaves which have just unfolded.

133 Fagus sylvatica *Beech*
A tall tree with ovate, elliptical leaves. The male catkins are ball-shaped and drooping. The female flowers are in pairs, surrounded by a 4-lobed cup which also contains the triangular nuts. Native in England where it is characteristic of chalk and limestone areas, planted in the north. Flowers in May, at the same time as the leaves appear.
On the colour plate there is a flowering twig on the left and a twig with ripe fruits on the right, sketched in the autumn.

134 Quercus robur *Common Oak, 'Pendunculate Oak'*
A large, robust tree with fissured bark and oblong, pinnately lobed leaves. The male flowers are held in hanging catkins, the female flowers on erect, few-flowered stems. The acorns are in small cups. Common in woods and hedge-rows on heavy soil such as clay and loam. Flowers in May, when the leaves appear.

135 Ulmus glabra *Wych Elm*
A tall tree with sharply serrate, obovate leaves rough on the upper surface, slightly hairy below. The small, red bisexual flowers are held in round heads. The seeds are surrounded by a broad wing. Common in woods and hedges throughout the British Isles, especially in the west and north. Flowers in April before the leaves are out.
On the colour plate, top left, there is a flowering twig and under it, ripe fruits and on the far right, a twig with leaves.

136 Humulus lupulus *Hop*
A herbaceous twining plant up to 6 m (19 ft) long with 3-5-lobed leaves. Male and female flowers are on different plants, the male flowers in a panicle, the female flowers in small catkins which later develop into so-called

'cones'. Grows in thickets and hedges; the female plants are extensively cultivated. Flowers June-July.

137 Urtica urens *Small Nettle*

A 10-40 cm (4-16 ins.) high, annual plant with fresh green, oval, serrate leaves covered with stinging hairs. The inconspicuous, unisexual flowers are held in small heads in the angles of the leaves, male and female intermixed. Native but rather local; a weed in gardens.

138 Urtica dioica *Stinging Nettle*

A 60-100 cm (24-40 ins.) high perennial plant with dull green, pointed, serrate leaves and stinging hairs. Male and female flowers grow on different plants. Common on roadsides, in hedgerows and near dwellings; also grows in moist woods. Flowers July-August.

139 Viscum album *Mistletoe*

A small, much-branched, parasitic shrub with evergreen, narrowly obovate leaves and inconspicuous, yellowish-green, unisexual flowers. Berries white. Parasitic on various trees, especially apple trees. Native; on the branches of a variety of deciduous trees, chiefly in England, but also cultivated. The colour plate shows a twig of a female plant with ripe berries, sketched in winter.

140 Rumex crispus *'Curled Dock'*

A 40-80 cm (16-24 ins.) high plant with narrow leaves, crinkled at the edges and small, greenish or reddish flowers in densely flowered, branched spikes. Common on waste or cultivated land throughout the British Isles. Flowers July-August.

141 Rumex obtusifolius
'Broad-leaved Dock'

An erect, 70-100 cm (28-40 ins.) high plant with small greenish flowers in sparsely-flowered inflorescence with spreading branches. The radical leaves are large and broad, the base is heart shaped and the point rounded. Common on waste ground and the margins of fields throughout the British Isles. Flowers July-August.

On the colour plate can be seen the top of a flowering plant and on the right, a basal leaf.

142 Rumex domesticus
'Long-leaved Dock'

A 60-100 cm (24-40 ins.) high plant with pale green flowers in a compact and many-flowered inflorescence. The radical leaves are broadly lanceolate with wavy edges. Occurs in ditches and damp places, chiefly from the midlands northwards. Flowers June-July. The colour plate shows a radical leaf and the top of a flowering plant.

143 Rumex thyrsiflorus
'Pyramid-flowered Dock'

A 44-90 cm. (18 ins.-1 ft.) high plant with a much branched, many-flowered inflorescence, the flowers greenish or red. The leaves are narrow and have 2 protruding lobes or auricles at the base. Common on roadsides and commons. Flowers July-August.

144 Rumex acetosa *Sorrel*

A plant 50-80 cm (20-32 ins.) high with an open spike of reddish flowers. The leaves are oblong and have 2 downward-pointing auricles at the base. Common in grassland and open places in woods. Flowers May-June.

145 Rumex acetosella
Sheep's Sorrel

A 15-30 cm (6-12 ins.) high plant with slender stems often tinged with red and inconspicuous flowers in an open inflorescence. The leaves are narrow and have 2 spreading lobes at the base. Common weed in sandy fields and on dry downs and in forest clearings. Flowers June-August.

146 Oxyria dygyna
'Mountain Sorrel'

A 10-30 cm (4-12 ins.) high plant with kidney-shaped leaves in a rosette and drooping flowers in a leafless inflorescence with few branches; chiefly found in the north of the British Isles. Flowers June-August.

147 Polygonum viviparum
'Viviparous Polygonum'

A 10-30 cm (4-12 ins.) high plant with an erect stem and a terminal spike of small, white or pink flowers. At the base the flowers are replaced by bulbils. On sand or shingle above high water mark; rare, chiefly in southern England. Flowers June-August.

148 Polygonum aviculare
Knotgrass, Knotweed

A prostrate, annual plant with branches 10-60 cm (4-24 ins.) long, small oval leaves and inconspicuous, reddish flowers in the axils of the leaves. Common in waste places, arable land and on the sea shore. Flowers July-September.

149 Polygonum convolvulus
Black Bindweed

An annual with twining or prostrate stems, 15-100 cm (6-40 ins.) long, heart-shaped leaves and small, greenish flowers in clusters. Common weed in fields, waste places and gardens. Flowers July-August.

150 Polygonum hydropiper
Water-pepper

A 30-50 cm (12-20 ins.) high plant with narrow leaves and small flowers in nodding spikes. The plant has a biting, acrid taste. Fairly common in damp places, ponds and ditches. Flowers July-September.

151 Polygonum amphibium
'Amphibious Bistort'

A perennial which is very variable; there are aquatic and terrestrial forms. As a water plant it has oblong, smooth, floating leaves and pink flowers in spikes. Common in pools and slow-flowing rivers or on banks near water; it may also occur in drier places and then has erect stems, up to 50 cm (20 ins.) high with narrower and somewhat rougher leaves. Flowers July-September.

152 Polygonum persicaria
'Persicaria'

A 20-70 cm (8-28 ins.) tall annual plant with oblong leaves and pink flowers in erect spikes. The stipules which embrace the stems at the base of the leaf-stalks are hairy. Common weed in waste places and on cultivated land. Flowers July-September.

152a Polygonum lapathifolium
'Pale Persicaria'

Resembles *P. persicaria* but differs in having smooth stipules except at the edges which are hairy, and by the flowers being, generally, of a greenish-white colour, less often red. Common in similar places. Flowers July-September.

153 Chenopodium bonus-henricus
All-good, Good King Henry

A plant 30-70 cm (12-28 ins.) high with long, triangular leaves and small, greenish flowers in a long, branching spike. Introduced but naturalised near villages and farms. Flowers June-July.

154 Chenopodium album *Fat Hen*

A 20-80 cm (8-32 ins.) high, mealy-white plant with ovate, waxy leaves, with or without teeth, and small, green flowers in a branched, compound inflorescence. Native; a common weed in fields, gardens and waste places. Flowers June-September.

155   Atriplex littoralis *'Shore Orache'*

A 30-60 cm (12-24 ins.) high, branching plant with narrow leaves and small, green, unisexual flowers in spike-like inflorescences (male and female flowers intermixed). The female flowers have no perianth but are surrounded by 2 triangular sepals which later grow so as to cover the fruit. Common on sea shores. Flowers July-September.

156   Atriplex hastata *'Hastate Orache'*

Resembles the previous plant but differs in having larger, triangular spear-shaped leaves with a coarsely toothed edge. Common on sea shores and waste places; less frequent as a weed in cultivated soil. Flowers July-September.

157   Atriplex patula *'Common Orache'*

Resembles the foregoing *Atriplex* in habit, but can be recognized by its lower leaves which are narrower with a few coarse teeth at the base and otherwise entire. Native; common on cultivated ground and on beaches. Flowers July-September.

158   Salsola kali *Saltwort*

A prostrate plant, 15-30 cm (6-12 ins.) long with a much branched stem, cylindrical fleshy leaves ending in a spine and small, greenish flowers in the axils of the leaves. Fairly common on sandy shores. Flowers July-August.

159   Suaeda maritima
      'Herbaceous Seablite'

A glaucous or reddish plant, 10-30 cm (4-12 ins.) high, with thick, succulent leaves. Common on salt-marshes and

sea-shores. Flowers July-September.

160   Salicornia europaea
      Glasswort, Marsh Samphire

A 5-30 cm (2-12 ins.) high plant with thick, succulent, jointed, cylindrical, leafless stems and branches. The tiny flowers are produced in the nodes of the branches. Common on salt marshes, frequently inundated by the tide. Flowers August-September.

161   Stellaria holostea *'Satin Flower*
      Adder's Meat, 'Greater Stitchwort

A 15-30 cm (6-12 ins.) plant with brittle, quadrangular stems and narrow leaves with rough edges. The large white flowers have deeply cleft petals and 3 styles Common in woods and hedgerows. Flowers May-June.

162   Stellaria nemorum
      Wood Stitchwort

A decumbent plant, 15-30 cm (6-12 ins.) long, with a thick, hairy stem, heart shaped leaves and large, white, star shaped flowers. Fairly common in damp woods. Flowers June-July.

163   Stellaria pallustris
      'Marsh Stitchwort'

A completely smooth, glaucous blue plant, 15-25 cm (6-10 ins.), with slender stems, narrow leaves and fairly large, white flowers. Common in bogs. Flowers June-July.

164   Stellaria graminea
      'Lesser Stitchwort'

Resembles the previous plant but is fresh green in colour and has smaller flowers, the petals not much longer than the calyx. Common on dry heaths, grassy ground and in woods. Flowers June-August.

165   Stellaria media *Chickweed*

Has 5-20 cm (2-8 ins.) long stems

rostrate or erect, hairy on one side,
vate leaves and small, white flowers.
lative; common on cultivated ground
nd on the sea shore. Flowers through-
ut the year.

66   Cerastium alpinum
        'Alpine Mouse-ear Chickweed'

A prostrate plant, the stems 5-15 cm
2-6 ins.) long and woolly, and large
white flowers with cleft petals and 5
tyles. Native; a local, alpine plant on
igh mountains in N. Wales, the Lake
istrict and Scotland. Flowers July-
August.

67   Cerastium arvense
        'Field Mouse-ear Chickweed'

A prostrate, 10-20 cm (4-8 ins.) long
lant with downy-haired stems and
aves and large, white flowers. Fairly
ommon on dry banks and in grassland.
Flowers May-August.

68   Cerastium semidecandrum
        'Little Mouse-ear Chickweed'

A slender plant, 5-15 cm (2-6 ins.) high,
vith stickly, hairy stems branching
rom the base and small white flowers.
Common on dry, sandy soil. Flowers
April-May.

69   Cerastium caespitosum
        'Common Mouse-ear Chickweed'

A densely hairy plant with 10-30 cm
4-12 ins.) long, prostrate or upright
tems and comparatively small flowers.
Common in meadows, on commons
long roadsides and in fields. Flowers
May-September.

70   Arenaria trinerva
        'Thyme-leaved Sandwort'

A 10-40 cm (14-16 ins.) high plant with
lender, hairy stems, thin ovate, 3-
eined leaves and small flowers with
hort, entire petals. Common in woods.
Flowers May-June.

171   Arenaria serpyllifolia
         'Lesser Thyme-leaved Sandwort'

A 5-15 cm (2-6 ins.) high plant with
finely hairy, forked stems and small
ovate leaves. The petals are shorter
than the sepals. Common on chalk
downs and arable fields. Flowers
June-August.

172   Honckenya peploides
         'Sea Sandwort'

A prostrate plant with stems 5-10 cm
(2-4 ins.) long, the tips erect, with
smooth, fleshy, crowded, ovate leaves
and white flowers. Common all round
the British Isles on sandy seashores.
Flowers June-July.

173   Sagina nodosa
         'Knotted Pearlwort'

A tufted plant with slender upright
stems, or prostrate, 5-20 cm (2-8 ins.)
long, awl-shaped leaves and fairly
large, white flowers. Common throughout Great Britain but chiefly in the
north, on dry sandy or gravelly places.
Flowers July-August.

174   Sagina procumbens
         'Procumbent Pearlwort'

A delicate, tufted plant with procumbent, rooting stems 2-5 cm (1-2 ins.),
small slender leaves and tiny green
flowers. Common in fields and meadows, on roadsides and among paving
stones. Flowers May-August.

175   Spergularia rubra
         Sand-spurrey

A procumbent plant with 5-15 cm
(2-6 ins.) long stems, flat, linear leaves
and small pink flowers. Common in
sandy fields and pastures, dislikes lime.
Flowers May-July.

176   Spergularia salina
         'Sea Sand-spurrey'

An annual plant, stems 5-15 cm (2-6

ins.) long with smooth, fleshy leaves and small pink or white flowers. Common on sandy salt marshes all round the coast. Flowers July-September.

176a Spergularia marginata
'*Winged-seed Sand-spurrey*'

Resembles the previous plant but is more robust and has larger flowers and can otherwise be recognised by its seeds which have a broad, scarious, winged edge. Grows in similar places but is less common. Flowers July-September.

177 Spergularia arvensis
Corn Spurrey

A 10-40 cm (4-16 ins.) high plant with erect stems and whorls of linear leaves and white flowers. Native; a common weed on arable land. Flowers June-September.

178 Herniaria glabra
'*Glabrous Rupture-wort*'

A small prostrate plant with 5-25 cm (2-10 ins.) long stems spreading flat along the ground, small oval leaves and inconspicuous, yellowish-green flowers in dense whorls in the axils of the leaves. Native, but rare and local in dry sandy places from Devonshire to Cumberland. Flowers June-July.

179 Scleranthus annuus
'*Annual Knawel*'

An annual plant with 3-20 cm (1-8 ins.) long stem, branched and prostrate or erect, with short awl-shaped leaves and very small, green flowers in the axils of the leaves. Common on dry sandy places and waste land. Flowers April-September.

180 Scleranthus perennis
'*Perennial Knawel*'

Resembles the previous species but differs in having tougher, erect stems

with densely packed flowers whose calyx has a broad, white, scarious edge. Rare; in dry fields in Norfolk and Suffolk. Flowers June-August.

181 Silene acaulis *Moss Campion*

Forms low, dense, mossy cushions. On mountain ledges and screes in N Wales, the Lake District and in Scotland. Flowers July-August.

182 Silene nutans
Nottingham Catchfly

Has narrow leaves and viscid, hairy stems 30-45 cm (12-18 ins.) high. The nodding, yellowish-white flowers do not open until evening; in the daytime the flowers look withered. A local plant on dry slopes, rocks and walls. Flowers June-July.

183 Silene cucubalus
Bladder Campion

A smooth, bluish-green plant, 25-45 cm (10-18 ins.) high with narrow leaves and nodding, white flowers with large, inflated calyx. Common on dry grassy land and roadsides throughout Great Britain and Ireland. Flowers June-August.

184 Silene rupestris '*Rock Campion*'

A 10-25 cm (4-10 ins.) high plant with slender, forked stems and small white or pink flowers. Not a native but sometimes grown in gardens.

185 Lychnis flos-cuculi
Ragged Robin

A 25-60 cm (10-24 ins.) high plant with narrow leaves and red flowers, the petals of which are deeply lobed. Common in wet meadows, marshes and fens. Flowers June-July.

186 Melandrium rubrum
Red Campion

A soft-haired plant, 25-60 cm (10-24

ns.) high with elliptical leaves and
nisexual flowers with red, deeply cleft
etals. Male and female flowers on
ifferent plants. Locally abundant in
he British Isles but rare in some dis-
ricts; in woods and on well drained
oils. Flowers May-August.

87 Melandrium album
White Campion

A plant 30-80 cm (12-32 ins.) high with
arge, sweet-scented flowers which
open only in the evening. Fairly com-
non in dry fields and on roadsides.
Flowers June-September.

The colour plate shows, at the
bottom, a flowering shoot of a female
plant and above, can be seen a single
male flower.

88 Viscaria alpina
'Red Alpine Catchfly'

A smooth plant, 15-30 cm (6-12 ins.)
high, with narrow leaves and densely
clustered, rose-pink flowers. Native
but a very rare plant of the Lake
District and Angus. Flowers July-
August.

89 Viscaria vulgaris
'Red German Catchfly'

A plant 20-45 cm (8-18 ins.) high with
narrow leaves, below which the stem is
blackish-red and sticky. Flowers red,
in a densely-flowered inflorescence.
Native but very rare, on cliffs and dry
rocks in N. Wales and Scotland.
Flowers June-July.

90 Saponaria officinalis
Soapwort, Bouncing Bett

A robust plant, 30-80 cm (12-32 ins.)
high, with elliptical leaves and a many-
flowered inflorescence of large, pink
(more rarely white) flowers which are
often double. Native in Devon and
Cornwall; probably a garden escape
elsewhere. Flowers July-September.

191 Dianthus superbus
'Garden Pink'

A 20-50 cm (8-20 ins.) high plant with
very narrow leaves and large mauve
flowers with lobed petals. Not native, a
garden escape. Flowers July-September.

192 Dianthus deltoides
Maiden Pink

Has 15-20 cm (6-8 ins.) high stems with
few flowers and narrow leaves. The
petals are dark red with white spots and
a toothed edge. Fairly common in dry
fields and downs. Flowers June-August.

193 Agrostemma githago
Corn Cockle

An annual plant 50-90 cm (20-36 ins.)
high with narrow leaves and large,
purple flowers with long calyx lobes.
Introduced; a weed in corn fields.

194 Nymphaea alba
White Water-lily

A water plant rooted in the mud, with
almost circular, floating leaves, reddish
underneath, and large white flowers
about 10 cm (4 ins.) across, and fleshy,
round fruits. Fairly common in lakes
and ponds. Flowers June-August.

195 Nuphar lutes *Yellow Water-lily,*
Brandy-bottle

Differs from the previous species in
having oval, floating leaves, green on
both sides, yellow flowers (4-6 cm
(2-3 ins.) across), and bottle-shaped
fruits. Common in similar places.
Flowers June-August.

196 Ceratophyllum demersum
Hornwort

A rootless, submerged water-plant with
the five linear leaves in a whorl. The
small flowers are unisexual, in the axils
of the leaves and are pollinated under
water. Fairly common in ponds and
ditches. July-September.

197 Berberis vulgaris *Barberry*

A shrub 1-2.5 m (30 ins.- 7 ft) high, with branched spines, ovate, toothed leaves in clusters and yellow flowers in drooping racemes. Berries red. Possibly native but very local; formerly planted for its edible fruit. Flowers May-June.

198 Thalictrum flavum
'*Common Meadow Rue*'

A plant up to 0.5-1 metre (20 ins.-3 ft) high with leaves twice or thrice pinnately divided and a many-flowered inflorescence of small, pale yellow flowers. Common in wet meadows and fens. Flowers in July.

199 Thalictrum alpinum
'*Alpine Meadow Rue*'

A small plant, 8-15 cm (3-6 ins.) in height, with a narrow spike of small, nodding flowers. Chiefly on rocky slopes and ledges in Great Britain. Flowers in July.

200 Thalictrum dunense
'*Lesser Meadow Rue*'

A plant 15-40 cm (6-16 ins.) high with a sinuous, much branched stem and nodding, greyish-violet flowers in loose racemes. Grows on dunes and on sandy sea-shores, especially in the north and west. Flowers July-August.

201 Actaea spicata
Baneberry, Herb Christopher

A branched plant 30-60 cm (12-24 ins.) high, with large horizontal, 3-lobed leaves, small white flowers in short spikes and black berries. Local on limestone in Yorkshire, Lancashire and Westmorland. Flowers May-June. *This plant is poisonous.*

202 Caltha palustris
Kingcup, Marsh Marigold

A glabrous, 15-30 cm (6-24 ins.) high plant with roundish leaves and large, yellow flowers. Common in marshes and wet meadows. Flowers April-May. *Poisonous when fresh.*

203 Trollius europaeus
Globe Flower

A plant 30-60 cm (12-24 ins.) high, with palmate leaves and large, almost globular flowers, pale yellow in colour. Locally common in wet meadows in mountainous districts. Flowers May-July. *Poisonous when fresh.*

204 Delphinium consolida
'*Forking Larkspur*'

A plant up to 20-40 cm (8-16 ins.) with narrow, palmate leaves and dark blue flowers in a few-flowered raceme. Introduced; a rare casual in cornfields and waste places. Flowers June-July. *This plant is poisonous.*

205 Aconitum septentrionale
'*Northern Monkshood*'

A robust, 1-2 m. (3-6 ins.) high plant with large palmate leaves and a long erect spike of violet flowers. Not a native, but may be found as a garden escape. *This plant is extremely poisonous.*

206 Pulsatilla pratensis
'*Meadow Anemone*'

A silky-haired plant with narrowly lobed, radical leaves and 10-30 cm (4-12 ins.) high flower-stems with a single, nodding, dark violet flower whose petals are about the same length as the stamens. Grows on downs and sandy fields, very rare. Flowers April-May. *The Pulsatilla species are poisonous when fresh.*

207 Pulsatilla vulgaris (Anemone pulsatilla) '*Pasque Flower*'

Resembles the previous species but differs in having erect, solitary flowers with perianth leaves of a paler colour and almost twice as long as the stamens.

A local plant found chiefly in Eastern England on dry slopes on limestone; uncommon. Flowers April-May.

208 Pulsatilla vernalis
'Spring Pasque Flower'

A shaggy plant with pinnate basal leaves and flower-stalks 5-15 cm (2-6 ins.) long with large flowers, reddish brown or purple outside, white inside. Not a native but grown in gardens. Flowers April-May.

209 Anemone nemorosa
Wood Anemone

Has a horizontal, rooting stem, palmate basal leaves and 10-25 cm (4-10 ins.) high, 1-flowered stems with 3 palmate, involucral bracts half way up and ending in a white flower, often tinged with red on the outside. Common in woods. Flowers April to May. *The Anemone species are poisonous when fresh.*

210 Anemone ranunculoides
'Yellow Wood Anemone'

Resembles the foregoing species in habit but differs in having yellow flowers, sometimes 2-3 together on the flower stems. Introduced; naturalised in a few localities in England. Flowers April-May.

211 Anemone hepatica *(Hepatica triloba)* 'Blue Anemone', *Hepatica*

Has a rosette of 3-lobed leaves and blue flowers on 5-15 cm (2-6 ins.) long stalks. The flowers are surrounded by green, ovate involucres. Not a native but frequently cultivated in England where there are many varieties.

212 Myosurus minimus *Mouse tail*

A small, annual plant with linear radical leaves and many erect flowering stems 5-12 cm (2-6 ins.) long, bearing tiny, yellowish flowers. When ripe, the receptacle elongates considerably like a long 'tail', on which numerous carpels are arranged in a spiral. Probably native but local, in damp arable fields. Flowers April-June.

213 Batrachium aquatilis
'Water Crowfoot'

A water plant with lax, hair-like sub-merged leaves and lobed floating leaves; the flowers are fairly large; the petals white with a yellow base. Common in ponds and ditches. Flowers May-July.

214 Ranunculus pygmaeus
'Pygmy Ranunculus'

A delicate plant, only a few centimetres high, with palmately lobed leaves and tiny, yellow flowers. Not found in the British Isles. Flowers July-August.

215 Ranunculus glacialis
'Ice Ranunculus'

A 5-15 cm (2-6 ins.) high plant with palmately-pinnate leaves and fairly large white flowers which become reddish-violet later. Not found in the British Isles. Flowers July-August.

216 Ranunculus lingua
Great Spearwort

A fen plant, 0.5-1 m (20 ins.-3 ft) high, with long, narrow leaves and large, golden flowers. Local in marshes and fens. Flowers June-August. *The Ranunculus species all have an acrid taste and are poisonous when fresh.*

217 Ranunculus auricomus
Goldilocks

A 20-40 cm (8-16 ins.) high plant with stalked, kidney-shaped, lobed basal leaves and sessile, deeply divided stem-leaves with narrow segments. The flowers are yellow, on round, hairy stalks and often the petals are not fully developed. Common in woods, occasionally on rocks. Flowers April-June.

218 Ranunculus acris
'Meadow Buttercup'

A hairy plant with a stem 20-70 cm (8-28 ins.) high with palmately lobed leaves and yellow flowers on thick stalks. Common in meadows and pastures and on roadsides. Flowers May-July.

219 Ranunculus flammula
Lesser Spearwort

Has erect stems 15-30 cm (6-12 ins.) high, with narrow leaves and yellow flowers on grooved stalks. Common in wet places. Flowers June-August.

220 Ranunculus ficaria
Lesser Calandine, Pilewort

A 10-25 cm (4-10 ins.) high plant with club-shaped tubers, heartshaped leaves and yellow flowers. Common in moist woods and hedgerows. Flowers April-May.

221 Ranunculus repens
'Creeping Buttercup'

Has runners which root at the nodes and flowering stems 20-45 cm (8-18 ins.) high. The leaves are divided into 3 with stalked, lobed segments. The flowers are yellow and have grooved stalks and reflexed sepals. Common in ditches and meadows, in moist places in woods and as a weed in wet fields. Flowers May-July.

222 Ranunculus bulbosus
'Bulbous Buttercup'

A hairy plant with a 15-20 cm (6-8 ins.) high stem, thickened at the base into the shape of a bulb. The leaves are palmate, with stalked, lobed segments. The flowers are yellow, on grooved stalks and with reflexed sepals. Common on dry, uncultivated downs and sandy fields. Flowers May-June.

223 Ranunculus sceleratus
'Celery-leaved Crowfoot'

An almost smooth plant, 15-60 cm (6-24 ins.) high with a thick, hollow stem, palmately lobed leaves and small, pale yellow flowers. Common in slow streams and boggy places. Flowers June-August.

224 Chelidonium majus
Greater Celandine

A sparsely hairy plant, 30-50 cm (12-20 ins.) with orange-yellow milky juice, pinnate leaves and yellow flowers in an umbel. The fruits are long, the pods narrow. Fairly common on walls and in hedgerows; an old medicinal plant. Flowers May-June. *This plant is poisonous.*

225 Papaver rhoeas *'Field Poppy'*

A stiff-haired plant 20-60 cm (8-24 ins.) high, with pinnate leaves, the lobes toothed and pointed. The flowers are large, red and the fruit is an almost globular, smooth capsule. Native or introduced; a fairly common weed in fields and waste places. Flowers June-July.

226 Papaver dubium
'Long-headed Poppy'

Resembles the previous plant but generally has slightly smaller and paler flowers and can otherwise be recognised by its flowering stems which have flattened hairs, and its capsule being club-shaped and smooth. Native or introduced; a weed of arable land and waste places. Flowers June-July.

227 Papaver argemone
'Long Prickly-headed Poppy'

An annual plant, 20-45 cm (8-18 ins.) high, with flattened hairs and bipinnate leaves. The flowers have scarlet petals with a large black blotch at their base. The capsule is club-shaped, with a few stiff hairs. Native or introduced; on light soils in the south, rarer in the north. Flowers May-July.

228 Corydalis cava
'Hollow Corydalis'

Has a large, hollow, subterranean tuber and stems 15-30 cm (6-12 ins.) high, bearing leaves twice divided into 3 segments, and a terminal raceme of reddish-violet or white, irregular flowers. Grows in woods. A rare escape from gardens. Flowers May-June.

229 Corydalis fabacea
'Small Corydalis'

A 5-15 cm (2-6 ins.) high plant with a small, solid tuber and a short, nodding cluster of reddish-violet flowers. Not native. Flowers in April.

230 Fumaria officinalis
'Common Fumitory'

A 10-30 cm (4-12 ins.) high plant with slender, much branched stems, finely divided, glaucous leaves and small, pale pink flowers in erect spikes. Native; on light soils and cultivated land. Flowers May-August.

231 Brassica campestris
Turnip, Naven

A 26-60 cm (8-24 ins.) high plant, somewhat glaucous, the lowest leaves pinnately lobed and sparsely hairy, the upper leaves smooth and entire, clasping the stem with their bases. The flowers are yellow and have spreading sepals. The fruit is a pod or siliqua. Probably introduced; a common weed throughout Great Britain and Ireland. Flowers June-July.

232 Sinapis arvensis
Charlock, 'Wild Mustard'

An annual plant 30-60 cm (1-2 ft) high with stiff hairs and pinnately lobed leaves or coarsely toothed, and yellow flowers with spreading sepals. The fruit is a pod (or siliqua) with 3-nerved valves. Probably native; a common weed of arable land. Flowers May-July.

233 Raphanus raphanistrum
Wild Radish, White Charlock

An annual plant 3-50 cm (1-20 ins.) high with stiff yellow, often with violet-veined petals and erect, adpressed sepals. The fruit is a jointed siliqua shaped like a string of pearls. Doubtfully native; fairly common especially in fields poor in lime. Flowers June-July.

234 Erysimum cheiranthoides
Treacle Mustard

A 25-60 cm (10 ins.-2 ft) high plant with narrow, entire or slightly toothed leaves, fairly small yellow flowers and pods 4-angled, with sharp edges. Probably introduced; locally common as a weed on sandy soils. Flowers June-August.

235 Diplotaxis muralis *Wall Rocket, Wall Mustard, Stinkweed*

A 25-60 cm (10 ins.-2 ft) high plant with radical, pinnate leaves, yellow flowers and flat pods with 2 rows of seeds in each. Introduced in Southern England, on limestone rocks and walls. Flowers July-September.

236 Cakile maritima *Sea Rocket*

A glabrous, fleshy plant with stems 20-40 cm (8-16 ins.) long, much branched and procumbent at their base, pinnate leaves and purple flowers. The fruit is a siliqua or pod, with 2 joints. Native; common on sandy sea-shores. Flowers July-September.

237 Lepidium ruderale
Narrow-leaved Pepperwort

A 15-30 cm (6-12 ins.) high, much

branched plant with a strong unpleasant smell. The small, greenish flowers are arranged in many-flowered racemes and are followed by small, flat, oval pods. Native; in waste places in England, rare in Scotland, absent from Ireland. Flowers June-August.

238   Barbarea vulgaris
'Winter Cress', 'Yellow Rocke

An erect, glabrous plant, 30-60 cm (1-2 ft) high, with pinnate or pinnately-lobed leaves and dense inflorescences of numerous, quite small yellow flowers. The pods are long and slender. On banks and in hedges, commoner in the south than in the north.

239   Crambe maritima *Seakale*

A robust, glabrous, glaucous blue plant, 30-60 cm (1-2 ft) high, with large, cabbage-like leaves, white flowers and round fruits. Grows on cliffs, sands and stoney sea-shores. Flowers June-July.

240   Bunias orientalis
'Warty Cabbage'

A 60-125 cm (2-4 ft) high plant with prickly hairs and pinnatifid or pinnately-lobed leaves and a close spike of numerous yellow flowers; pods asymetrical, warty. Introduced, a casual; used as salad or a fodder plant. Flowers June-August.

241   Nasturtium microphyllum
'One-rowed Watercress'

A fen plant, 30-50 cm (12-20 ins.) tall, with lax, brittle stems, pinnate leaves, white flowers and curved pods. Common throughout the British Isles near streams and in ditches. Flowers June-July.

242   Rorippa amphibia
'Great Yellow Cress'

A 50-120 cm (20 ins.-4 ft) high bog plant with pinnatifid or entire leaves, toothed at the edges, small, yellow flowers and short, elliptical pods. Locally common in ponds and ditches. Flowers June-July.

243   Rorippa islandica
Marsh Yellow Cress

A 10-50 cm (4-20 ins.) high plant with slender, branched stems, pinnatifid leaves, small, pale yellow flowers and oblong siliqua. Common in moist places on the margins of ponds and ditches. Flowers June-August.

244   Cardamine pratensis
Cuckoo Flower, Lady's Smock

A plant 20-45 cm (8-18 ins.) high with pinnate leaves and large, mauve flowers with yellow stigmas. Common in damp meadows. Flowers May-June.

245   Cardamine amara
'Large Bitter Cress'

Very similar to the above but the flowers have purple stigmas. Grows throughout the British Isles near springs and in other moist places. Flowers May-June.

246   Dentaria bulbifera *Coral-wort*

A 40-50 cm (16-20 ins.) high plant with pinnate leaves and large, purple, pale pink or, rarely, white flowers. There are brownish-violet bulbils in the axils of the leaves. Very local in woods, generally on chalky soil. Flowers May-June.

247   Alliaria petiolata
Garlic Mustard, Jack-by-the-Hedge

A plant 40-70 cm (16-28 ins.) high, smelling of garlic, with heart-shaped, toothed leaves, white flowers and long pods. Common in hedges and thickets. Flowers May-June.

248   Turritis glabra *Tower Mustard*

An erect, glaucous plant, 70-100 cm

(28-40 ins.) high with arrow-shaped leaves clasping the stem, pale yellow flowers and long, thin siliquas or pods. Local on dry banks in Eastern England, rare in S.W. England and Scotland; absent from Wales. Flowers June-July.

249 Berteroa incana *'Hoary Alison'*

An annual plant, 25-45 cm (10-18 ins.) high with oval leaves which are whitish-grey with stellate hairs. The flowers are white with deeply cleft petals; the pods are oval. Introduced; naturalised in sandy fields and waste places. Flowers May-August.

250 Thlaspi arvense
'Field Penny-cress'

A glabrous plant, 15-30 cm (6-12 ins.) high, with oblong leaves, small white flowers and flat, round pods. Doubtfully native; a weed on arable land and in waste places. Flowers May-July.

251 Thlaspi alpestre
'Alpine Penny-cress'

A plant 10-30 cm (4-12 ins.) high, with a basal rosette of spathulate leaves on long stalks and smaller leaves up the stem, small white flowers and flat, wedgeshaped pods. Native, but local on limestone, usually on mountains. Flowers May-June.

252 Capsella bursa-pastoris
Shepherd's Purse

A plant 10-40 cm (4-16 ins.) high with pinnatifid or almost entire, radical leaves, arrow-shaped stem-leaves, small, white flowers and flat triangular pods. A common weed on cultivated land and waste places. Flowers April-September.

253 Arabis arenosa
'Sand Rock-cress'

A 10-30 cm (4-12 ins.) high plant with a rosette of pinnate, radical leaves. The stem leaves are oblong and the flowers are whitish-mauve and rather large. The pods are long and narrow. Not native in the British Isles but sometimes grown in gardens. Flowers May-June.

254 Arabis hirsuta *'Hairy Rock cress'*

An erect, hairy plant, 20-40 cm (8-16 ins.) high with oblong, toothed leaves, small white flowers and long erect, adpressed pods. Common on chalk and limestone slopes and dry banks. Flowers May-June.

255 Arabidopsis thaliana
Thale Cress, 'Common Wall Cress'

A slender plant, 10-25 cm (4-10 ins.) high, with oblong radical leaves in a rosette, tiny, white flowers and thin pods. Common on dry fields and downs. Flowers April-May.

256 Draba alpina
'Alpine Whitlow Grass'

A small plant 5-10 cm (2-4 ins.) high with a rosette of radical leaves, yellow flowers and oval pods. Does not occur in the British Isles. Flowers June-July.

257 Erophila verna *Whitlow Grass*

A delicate, little plant, 2-15 cm (1-6 ins.) high, with a rosette of radical leaves and small white flowers with cleft petals. The pods are oval. Common in dry fields and on rocks and walls. Flowers March-May.

258 Subularia aquatica *Awlwort*

A small, aquatic annual plant, 2-5 cm (1-2 ins.) high with awl-shaped leaves, small white flowers and oval pods. Native but local throughout the British Isles, in lakes and pools. Flowers July-August.

259 Alyssum alyssoides
Small Alison

An annual plant, 10-20 cm (4-8 ins.)

high with whitish-grey hairs, tongue-shaped leaves, small, pale yellow flowers and flat, circular pods. Introduced; found occasionally in fields and on arable land in southern England and eastern Scotland. Flowers May-June.

260 Cochlearia officinalis
Scurvy Grass

A plant 15-30 cm (6-12 ins.) tall with roundish leaves, white flowers and almost globula pods. Common on salt-marshes and on the sea shore. Flowers May-June.

261 Teesdalia nudicaulis
'Shepherd's Cress'

A small annual plant, 5-15 cm (2-6 ins.), with pinnately lobed radical leaves, small white flowers and oval pods. Locally common on dry, sandy ground. Flowers April-June.

262 Sisymbrium sophia *Flixweed*

A plant 50-80 cm (20-32 ins.) high with very finely divided leaves, small, greenish-yellow flowers and long thread-like pods. Doubtfully native; on waste places and roadsides, not common. Flowers June-August.

263 Sisymbrium officinale
Hedge Mustard

A plant 30-50 cm (12-20 ins.) high with stiff, spreading branches, pinnate-lobed leaves, small yellow flowers and erect, adpressed, awl-shaped pods. Fairly common in hedgebanks, by roadsides and in waste places throughout Great Britain. Flowers June-July.

264 Camelina sativa
Gold of Pleasure

A plant 30-80 cm (12-32 ins.) high, with arrow-shaped leaves, small, pale yellow flowers and ovoid pods. Introduced; occasionally found in fields amongst crops. Flowers July-August.

265 Sedum album *'White Stonecrop'*

A glabrous plant 10-15 cm (4-6 ins.), often tinged with red, with small succulent leaves and white flowers. May be a native in the Malverns, Mendips and in Devon, naturalised in other places in the British Isles. Flowers July-August.

266 Sedum telephium
Orpine, Livelong

A perennial plant 20-50 cm (8-20 ins.) high with oval, fleshy leaves and a dense corymb of small, yellowish-green flowers. Fairly common in most of the British Isles but becoming rare in Scotland, on hedgebanks, walls and in woods. Flowers August-September.

267 Sedum rosea
Rose-root, Midsummer-men

A glaucous plant 10-30 cm (4-12 ins.) high, with thick, elliptical leaves and yellow flowers. Common in mountainous districts on rocks. Flowers June-July.

268 Sedum annuum
'Annual Stonecrop'

A small, annual plant 3-10 cm (1-4 ins.) high with thick leaves often with red spots, and small greenish-yellow flowers. Not a native but sometimes grown in gardens. Flowers June-August.

269 Sedum acre *Wall-pepper*

Grows in dense, cushion-shaped clumps consisting of erect stems 3-15 cm (1-6 ins.) with succulent, ovoid leaves. The yellow flowers are star-shaped. Common on dry sandy ground and on walls. Flowers June-July.

270 Saxifraga oppositifolia
'Purple Saxifrage'

A small plant with prostrate stems 2-5 cm (1-2 ins.) long, the small leaves densely packed in four rows, and fairly large, purple flowers. On damp rocks or stoney ground on mountains, in N. Wales and Yorkshire to Shetland. Flowers April-June.

271 Saxifraga tridactylites
Rue-leaved Saxifrage

An annual plant, 5-12 cm (2-5 ins.) high, the basal leaves being closely packed, those on the stem 3-lobed; the flowers are small and white. Grows on dry, sandy ground and on walls. Flowers May-June.

272 Saxifraga aizoides
'Yellow Mountain Saxifrage'

A plant 5-15 cm (2-6 ins.) high, the flowering stems erect, the sterile ones decumbent, bearing small, dense leaves and yellow or dark orange flowers. Besides streams and on wet stoney ground on mountains; chiefly in the north of the British Isles. Flowers July August.

273 Saxifraga nivalis
'Alpine Saxifrage'

A 10-30 cm (4-12 ins.) high plant with broad, thick toothed radical leaves and small, reddish-white flowers. On wet rocks on mountains, very local and rare. Flowers July-August.

274 Saxifraga rivularis
'Brook Saxifrage'

A small plant, 5-15 cm (2-6 ins.) high, with long-stalked, kidney-shaped leaves and white flowers. Very rare and local on wet rocks in parts of Scotland. Flowers July-August.

275 Saxifraga stellaris
'Starry Saxifrage'

A rosette plant, 5-15 cm (2-6 ins.)high, with wedge-shaped, toothed radical leaves and white, star-like flowers. Common in wet places on mountains. Flowers July-August.

276 Saxifraga granulata
'Meadow Saxifrage'

A plant 15-30 cm (6-12 ins.) high, with a glandular-hairy stem with bulbils at the base. The leaves have long stalks and are kidney-shaped with crenate edges. The flowers are white and fairly large. Common in pastures and on dry downs. Flowers May-June.

277 Saxifraga cotyledon
'Cup Saxifrage'

A beautiful plant, 20-50 cm (8-20 ins.) high, with a close rosette of radical leaves edged with small, white teeth, and a large branching inflorescence of white flowers. The flowering rosette dies but others are formed. Not a native but grown in rock gardens. Flowers July-August.

278 Saxifraga cernua
'Drooping Saxifrage'

A small, rosette plant, 10-20 cm (4-8 ins.) high with red bulbils in the upper axils of the leaves and a single, terminal, white flower. Native, but very rare; on rocks above 3,500 ft in Perthshire and Argyll. Flowers July-August.

279 Parnassia palustris
Grass of Parnassus

Has heart-shaped leaves and the stem is 10-30 cm (4-12 ins.) high, bearing a single leaf and ending in a large, white flower. Rather local, in marshes and on wet moors. Flowers July-September.

280 Chrysosplenium alternifolium
'Alternate-leaved Golden Saxifrage'

A 5-15 cm (2-6 ins.) high plant with kidney-shaped, round toothed leaves and small, yellow flowers in a flat, terminal cyme, surrounded by yellowish-green upper leaves. Native but local, chiefly in the north of the British Isles on wet rocks.

281 Ribes nigrum *Black Currant*

A shrub up to 1-2 m (3-6 ft), with pal-mately lobed, strong-smelling leaves and pendulous clusters of green flow-ers, reddish inside. Berries black. Native but often found as an escape from cultivation. Flowers May-June.

281a Ribes rubrum *Red Currant*

Resembles the previous species but the leaves have no scent; the small flowers are yellowish-green and the berries red. Doubtfully native, in woods and hedges; cultivated for its fruit. Flowers in May.

282 Ribes alpinum
'*Mountain Currant*'

A small bush with 3-lobed leaves and small, greenish-yellow flowers in erect clusters. The flowers are unisexual and the two sexes grow on distinct bushes. Berries red. Native in rocky woods on limestone but also an escape from cultivation. Flowers May-June.

283 Cotoneaster integerrima
'*Great Orme Berry*'

A low shrub with oval leaves, downy on the back; small, reddish-white flowers and red fruits. Native but only found now on Great Orme's Head, Carnavon. Flowers in May.

284 Crataegus oxyacantha
May, '*Midland Hawthorn*'

A thorny bush or small tree with 3-5-lobed leaves with their side veins curving inwards towards the central vein. The flowers are white, in dense corymbs; they generally have 2 styles. Fruits red with 2 stones. Native, in woods but much less common than *C. monogyna*. Flowers May-June.

284a Crataegus monogyna
Common Hawthorn

Resembles the above species but differs in having flowers with one style, and deeply lobed leaves, their side veins curving outwards. Common in thickets and hedges. Flowers in June.

285 Sorbus aucuparis
Rowan, Mountain Ash

A medium sized tree with unequally pinnate leaves and white flowers in large corymbs. Fruits red. Native; common in woods and on high moun-tain rocks in the north and west; rare and perhaps not native in the eastern and central counties of England. Flowers May-June.

286 Sorbus intermedia
'*Cut-leaved White Beam*'

A moderate-sized tree with pinnately-lobed leaves covered with grey down underneath. Flowers white and fruits red. Introduced; commonly planted and becoming naturalised in some areas. Flowers in June.

287 Malus sylvestris *Crab Apple*

A moderate-sized tree with elliptical, toothed leaves, glabrous underneath and reddish-white flowers. The fruits are small, round, hard, sour apples. Fairly common in woods and hedges. Flowers May-June.

288 Prunus spinosa *Blackthorn. Sloe*

A densely branched, thorny bush with numerous small, white flowers appear-ing before the leaves, which are obovate with a finely toothed edge and the fruits are blue-black with a bitter, astringent taste; each contains one round stone. Common in thickets and hedges. Flowers in May.

289 Prunus padus *Bird-cherry*

A bush or small tree with crinkled, saw-toothed leaves, white flowers in drooping clusters and small, black stone-fruits. Native; common in the north of England and Scotland in woods and thickets. Flowers in May.

290 Prunus avium
Gean, Wild Cherry

A tall tree with elliptical, toothed leaves and large bunches of white flowers. Fruits reddish-yellow or dark red, sweet, stone-fruits. Grows in woods and hedges; common in England and Wales, rarer in Scotland. Our cultivated, sweet cherries are improved forms of this species. Flowers in May.

291 Filipendula vulgaris *Dropwort*

A 50-70 cm (20-28 ins.) high plant with tuberous roots; the leaves are pinnate with lobed segments. The white flowers, reddish before opening, are held in a wide, terminal panicle. Native but rather local, though abundant where it occurs, on calcareous grassland; less frequent in Scotland. Flowers May-August.

292 Filipendula ulmaria
Meadow-sweet

A plant 0.5-1 m (18 ins.-3 ft) high, with pinnate leaves, grey and downy underneath, and small, yellowish-white flowers in a much branched inflorescence. Common in wet meadows, in ditches and in wet woods. Flowers June-July.

293 Agrimonia eupatoria
Common Agrimony

A plant up to 30-80 cm (1 ft-32 ins.), hairy and with pinnate leaves and yellow flowers in a long spike. Common on roadsides and along edges of fields. Flowers July-August.

294 Geum urbanum
Herb Bennet, Wood Avens

A plant 30-60 cm (1-2 ft) high, with pinnate, basal leaves and stem leaves divided into 3, having large, leaf-like

stipules. The flowers are erect, on long stalks, with yellow petals. Common in woods, scrub, hedgerows and other shady places on damp soil. Flowers June-August.

295 Geum rivale *Water avens*

A plant 15-45 cm (6-18 ins.) high, with pinnate leaves and nodding reddish flowers. Common in marshes, along ditches and in moist woods. Flowers May-June.

296 Dryas octopetala
'*Mountain Avens*'

A low, evergreen shrub with oblong, roundly toothed leaves and large, white flowers on 2-8 cm (1-3 ins.) long, erect stalks. When ripe, the long, hairy styles on the fruit stand up like plumes. Native but local, on rock ledges on mountains. Flowers July-August.

297 Alchemilla alpina
'*Alpine Lady's Mantle*'

A small plant, 5-15 cm (2-6 ins.) high, with palmate leaves and small, yellowish-green flowers in dense, terminal inflorescences. On mountains, chiefly in northern England and Scotland. Flowers June-August.

298 Alchemilla vulgaris
. *Lady's Mantle*

A variable plant, 15-30 cm (6-12 ins.) high, with palmately lobed leaves, toothed at the edges, and small, yellowish green flowers in terminal cymes. Common in damp grassland, on roadsides and in woods; rarer in S.E. England. Flowers June-August.

299 Aphanes arvensis *Parsley Piert*

A small, densely branched plant with procumbent stems, 5-10 cm (2-4 ins.) long; small, palmate leaves and insignificant, green flowers forming dense heads in the axils of the leaves.

Common weed in fields. Flowers May-August.

300 Sibbaldia procumbens
'Least Cinquefoil'

A small plant 3-5 cm (1-2 ins.), with basal leaves consisting of 3 leaflets, and small, yellowish-green flowers in terminal cymes. On mountain tops in northern England and in Scotland. Flowers July-August.

301 Fragaria vesca
Wild Strawberry

A sticky plant, 10-20 cm (4-8 ins.) high, producing long runners, the leaves consisting of 3 leaflets, and the flowers are white. The 'strawberries' are formed by the swollen, juicy, red receptacle on which the small, nut-like carpels are placed. The sepals are recurved after the flower has fallen. Common in woods and pastures on calcareous soils. Flowers May-June.

301a Fragaria viridis
'Green Wild Strawberry'

Resembles the previous species, but differs in having slightly larger, yellowish-white flowers, and by the calyx being adpressed to the ripe, red fruit. Grows on dry downs. Flowers May-June.

302 Potentilla reptans
Creeping Cinquefoil

Has runners 30-60 cm (1-2 ft) long, leaves with long stalks and 5 leaflets, and large yellow flowers on erect stems. Common in fields, on roadsides and waste places. Flowers June-August.

303 Potentilla anserina *Silverweed*

A silky-haired plant with pinnate leaves and stems 15-60 cm (6-24 ins.) long and large, yellow flowers held singly on erect stems. Common in fields and on road-sides, in damp pastures and on the

margins of lakes. Flowers May-July.

304 Potentilla verna
Spring Cinquefoil

A low, tuft-forming plant with 5-7-lobed basal leaves and 5-15 cm (2-6 ins.) long, sparsely branched stems with yellow flowers. Grows on dry downs, from Somerset to Angus, very local. Flowers in May.

305 Potentilla erecta
Common Tormentil

A plant with a thick, woody rootstock, red inside, slender, forked stems 10-30 cm (4-12 ins.) high, with 3-5-lobed leaves and yellow 4-petalled flowers on thin erect stalks. Common in grassland, on heaths, fens and in woods. Flowers June-August.

306 Potentilla argentea
'Hoary Cinquefoil'

A plant 15-30 cm (6-12 ins.) high, with close white hairs on the stems, which bear 5-lobed leaves with pinnate leaflets, which are also covered with silvery white hairs underneath. The small, pale yellow flowers are in terminal panicles. Local, especially in the west, on dry grassland and downs and dunes. Flowers June-July.

307 Potentilla norvegica
Norwegian Cinquefoil

A hairy plant with erect, forked stems, 25-40 cm (10-15 ins.) high, leaves divided into three and small, pale yellow flowers. Introduced and now naturalised, especially in S.E. England. Flowers June-August.

308 Potentilla fruticosa
Shrubby Cinquefoil

A low, much branched shrub with unequally pinnate leaves and large yellow flowers. Native but very local, on damp rocky ground. Flowers June to September.

309 Comarum palustre
'Marsh Cinquefoil'

Has reddish, decumbent stems, 30-80 cm (12-32 ins.) long, bearing unequally pinnate leaves, the leaflets serrate and glaucous beneath. The flowers are deep purple. Common on marshes and moors. Flowers June-July.

310 Rosa spinosissima
Burnet Rose

A low, much branched shrub with densely packed prickles mixed with stiff bristles, leaves with 3-5 pairs of leaflets and large flowers with cream-coloured petals. The hip is a blackish-brown colour and almost globular. Common on dunes and sandy heaths, generally near the sea. Flowers June-July.

311 Rosa canina *Dog-rose*

A tall bush, 1-3 m (3-10 ft) high with arching stems bearing many stout, curved or hooked prickles. The flowers are pink or almost white. The hips are red and oval. Common in hedges, woods and scrub; rare in Scotland. Flowers June-July.

312 Rubus idaeus *Raspberry*

An under-shrub with woody stems 1-2 m (3-6 ft) high, armed with thin, straight prickles. The stems are biennial. In the first year they produce leaves only; these are unequally pinnate with 3-5-7 leaflets, covered with silvery-white down underneath. The second year, flowering and leaf-bearing, short shoots are formed from the buds on the upright long shoot which dies down the following year. In the meantime, new long shoots have been formed from the root-stock of the plant. The flowers are small and white

in drooping clusters. The raspberry has a compound fruit consisting of a number of red carpels on a conical receptacle from which it separates when ripe. Common in woods and on heaths; grown in gardens for its fruit. Flowers in June.

313 Rubus fruticosus
Blackberry, Bramble

A woody plant with 1-3 cm (3-10 ft) long, very prickly, arched or prostrate stems, with a biennial cycle of development like the previous species. The long shoots have leaves consisting of 5 leaflets and, on the short shoots which bear the flowers, there are generally 3 leaflets. The flowers are white or pink. The fruit is a purplish black. Common in woods and hedges; cultivated in gardens for its fruit. Flowers June-August.

314 Rubus caesius *Dewberry*

Resembles the previous species but has more slender, creeping or rooting stems with a blue bloom, and weak prickles; leaves divided into 3, and white flowers in erect clusters. The fruits are black but look blue owing to a coating of wax. Common in woods and thickets and on grassland in England and Wales; local in Scotland. Flowers June-September.

315 Rubus saxatilis
'Stone Bramble'

A perennial plant with runners 10-30 cm (4-12 ins.) long, the flowering shoots erect with leaves divided into 3 leaflets. The small, white flowers are in terminal cymes. The fruits are scarlet. Rather local in woods and hilly districts. Flowers June-August.

316 Rubus arcticus
'Arctic Stone Bramble'

A delicate, 10-25 cm (4-10 ins.) high

herbaceous plant with 3 leaflets to each leaf and red flowers. The fruits are dark red. Not a native in the British Isles. Flowers in June.

317 Rubus chamaemorus
Cloudberry

A plant 8-10 cm (3-4 ins.) high, with kidney-shaped, 5-lobed leaves and a single, terminal, white flower. The fruits are orange-yellow. Grows on high moors, locally abundant. Flowers May-June.

318 Genista tinctoria
Dyer's Greenweed

A small shrub 20-60 cm (8 ins.-2 ft) high with green branches bearing narrow leaves and yellow flowers in dense, terminal clusters. The pods are flat and smooth. Fairly common in rough pastures in England and Wales, but rare in Scotland. Flowers July-August. *The seeds are poisonous.*

319 Genista anglica
Needle Furze, Petty Whin

A dwarf shrub 10-40 cm (4-16 ins.) high, with thin, spiney branches, small, ovate leaves and yellow flowers in short racemes. The pods are short and thick. Fairly common locally in Great Britain but rare in Scotland. Flowers May-June.

320 Sarothamnus scoparius *Broom*

A much-branched shrub 0.5-2 m (20 ins.-6 ft) high, with stiff, wiry, green, angled branches bearing small leaves, with 3 leaflets or entire, and large yellow flowers. The pods are black, flat and hairy. Grows on dry downs and heaths, throughout the British Isles. Flowers May-June. *The seeds are poisonous.*

321 Ononis repens *Restharrow*

A small shrub with procumbent stems, 30-60 cm (1-2 ft) long, slightly woody and sometimes spiney. The leaves are trifoliate and the flowers pink. Common on roadsides and on slopes and pastures. Flowers July-August.

322 Melilotus officinalis
'Common Melilot'

A plant 30-80 cm (12-32 ins.) high with straight, branched stems bearing trifoliate leaves and small, yellow flowers in long, narrow spikes. Introduced naturalised in S. England and Ireland. Flowers July-September.

323 Medicago sativa
Lucerne, Alfalfa

A plant 30-70 cm (12-28 ins.) with trifoliate leaves and racemes of purple flowers. The pods are twisted spirally. Introduced; grown for fodder and occurs as an escape from cultivation. Flowers July-September.

324 Medicago lupulina
Black Medick

A small, prostrate plant with thin stems 7-35 cm (3-14 ins.) long and small, pale yellow flowers in dense oval heads. The small, black pods are slightly coiled. Common in fields and on dry downs. Flowers June-September.

325 Medicago falcata
'Sickle Medick'

Has decumbent or erect stems, 15-50 cm (6-20 ins.) long, and yellow flowers in short racemes. The pods are curved and sickle-shaped. Native in Norfolk Suffolk and Cambridge in grassy places; introduced elsewhere. Flowers July-August.

326 Trifolium dubium
'Lesser Yellow Trefoil'

A procumbent plant with slender stems, trifoliate leaves and heads of 8-20 small, yellow flowers. As in all other species of the Clover genus, the withered petals remain after flowering, enclosing the small, 1-seeded or few-seeded pods. Common in grassy places throughout the British Isles but rarer in Northern Scotland. Flowers May-August.

327   Trifolium spadiceum
'Brown Clover'

A plant 10-40 cm (4-16 ins.) high, with erect stems and oblong heads with numerous flowers, yellow at first, then a shining chestnut brown. Not found in the British Isles. Flowers June-August.

328   Trifolium aureum
'Golden Trefoil'

A plant 15-30 cm (6-12 ins.) high with erect or decumbent stems and heads of numerous flowers, golden yellow at first, after flowering a faded brown. Introduced; naturalised in fields. Flowers July-September.

329   Trifolium campestre
'Hop Trefoil'

A slender plant with decumbent or erect stems, 15-30 cm (6-12 ins.) long and yellow flowers in 20-40-flowered heads. Common on dry fields and downs. Flowers May-August.

330   Trifolium pratense   Red Clover

The stems are 25-40 cm (10-16 ins.) long, decumbent or erect, with large, round heads of reddish-mauve or pink (more rarely white) flowers. Common in fields and meadows. Flowers May-September.

331   Trifolium medium
Zigzag Clover

Resembles the foregoing species, but can be recognised by its zigzag, decumbent or erect stems, up to 50 cm (20 ins.) long, narrower leaflets and flowers

of a darker red, in stalked, racemose heads. Grows on downs and in fields; rather local. Flowers June-July.

332   Trifolium hybridum
Alsike Clover

A plant 25-60 cm (10-24 ins.) tall with erect, branching stems and heads of flowers which are pale, rose-pink at first, brown when faded. Probably introduced; naturalised throughout the British Isles along roadsides. Flowers June-August.

333   Trifolium repens
White Clover, Dutch Clover

Stems 10-40 cm (4-16 ins.) long, procumbent and rooting. The white or pale reddish flowers are in rounded heads in erect, leafless stalks. Native; in grassy places throughout the British Isles. Flowers June-August.

334   Trifolium montanum
'Mountain Clover'

A plant 10-40 cm (4-16 ins.) high, with erect stems and rather small, white flower-heads. Grows on grassy downs and pastures, but does not occur in Great Britain. Flowers in July.

335   Trifolium fragiferum
'Strawberry Clover'

Resembles White Clover in habit, but differs in having small heads of reddish-white flowers where the calyx becomes inflated after flowering so that the whole head somewhat resembles a strawberry. Common on grassy place on heavy clay soils. Flowers July-August.

336   Trifolium arvense   Hare's-foot

An annual plant with erect, 10-25 cm (4-10 ins.) high, branched stems and small, pink flowers in feathery, oblong heads. Common on dunes and in dry fields and pastures. Flowers June-August.

337 Anthyllis vulneraria
Kidney-vetch, Ladies' Fingers

A plant, 10-30 cm (4-12 ins.) high with erect or decumbent stems, unequally pinnate leaves and terminal heads of yellow flowers with an inflated calyx covered with white hairs. Common on dry fields and downs on shallow soils. Flowers June-July.

338 Ornithopus perpusillus
Birdsfoot

An annual plant with decumbent, branched stems, 5-25 cm (2-10 ins.) long, with many pairs of unequally pinnate leaves and tiny white flowers, striped yellow and red. The curved pods are constricted between the seeds. Grows on poor, sandy ground; common in Great Britain except the north of Scotland and Ireland. Flowers June-July.

339 Lotus corniculatus
Birdsfoot Trefoil, Bacon and Eggs

Has decumbent and ascending, solid stems, 10-30 cm (4-12 ins.) high, trifoliate leaves and yellow flowers in 5-6-flowered, terminal umbels. Common in meadows and fields. Flowers June-July.

340 Lotus uliginosus
Large Birdsfoot Trefoil

Resembles the previous plant but differs in having erect, hollow stems, 20-50 cm (8-20 ins.) high and 7-15-flowered umbels. Grows in damp, grassy places. Flowers July-August.

341 Astragalus glycyphyllos
Milk-Vetch

Has robust, decumbent or ascending stems up to 3 ft in length, unequally pinnate leaves and greenish-yellow flowers in oval clusters. The leaves taste of liquorice. In rough grass and bushy places, local. Flowers June-July.

342 Astragalus alpinus
'Alpine Milk-vetch'

A plant 10-30 cm (4-12 ins.) tall with equally pinnate, many-paired leaves and bluish-purple flowers. In grassy places on mountains, rare. Flowers June-July.

343 Oxytropus campestris
'Yellow Oxytropus'

A plant 10-20 cm (4-8 ins.) high with unequal pinnate leaves in a rosette, and long-stalked heads of pale yellow (or reddish-yellow) flowers. Native but very rare, on rocks up to 2,000 ft. Flowers June-August.

344 Lathyrus pratensis
'Meadow Vetchling'

A creeping or climbing plant with an angular stem, 25-100 cm (10-40 ins.) long. The leaves have only one pair of leaflets and end in a tendril. The flowers are yellow, in long-stalked clusters. Common in hedges and grassy places. Flowers June-July.

345 Lathyrus montanus
'Bitter Vetch'

A plant 15-30 cm (6-12 ins.) high, with a smooth, winged stem and pinnate leaves ending in a short point. The flowers are pink at first, later bluish-purple. Grows in woods and on heaths. Native but very rare, in hilly country chiefly in the west and north.

346 Lathyrus maritimus *'Sea Pea'*

Has creeping, 20-40 cm (8-16 ins.) long stems and glaucous, pinnate leaves ending in tendrils. The flowers are red at first, later bluish purple. On shingle beaches but very local. Flowers July-August.

347 Lathyrus sylvestris
'Narrow-leaved Everlasting Pea'

A climbing plant with 1-2 m (3-6 ft) long, winged stems; the leaves have only 1 pair of leaflets and end in branched tendrils. The large, rose-pink flowers are 3-8 together on a long stalk. Grows in thickets and woods, local. Flowers July-August.

348 Lathyrus vernus 'Spring Pea'

A 20-40 cm (8-12 ins.) high plant with erect, angled stems and abruptly pinnate leaves of a fresh green colour. The flowers are red at first, later purple. Not found in the British Isles. Flowers May-June.

349 Vicia cracca *Tufted Vetch*

Has thin, climbing stems, 25-100 cm (10-40 ins.) long, and abruptly pinnate, many-paired leaves ending in tendrils. The bluish-purple flowers are in dense, one-sided racemes. Common in grassy places throughout the British Isles. Flowers June-August.

350 Vicia hirsuta *Hairy Tare*

A slender plant with 25-30 cm (10-12 ins.) long, climbing stems bearing leaves with 4-8 pairs of leaflets and ending in tendrils. The flowers are small and bluish white, the pods hairy and containing 2 seeds. Native, a common weed in fields and grassy places. Flowers May-July.

351 Vicia angustifolia
'Narrow-Leaved Vetch'

A plant 15-40 cm (6-16 ins.) high with abruptly pinnate leaves ending in tendrils. The dark-red flowers are in pairs in the axils of the leaves. A fairly common weed in fields and grassy places. Flowers May-June.

352 Vicia sepium 'Bush Vetch'

A plant 30-60 cm (1-2 ft) high with abruptly pinnate leaves ending in tendrils. The leaflets are oval. The flowers are a bluish purple, in short-stalked clusters in the axils of the leaves. Common in grassy places, woods and thickets. Flowers May-July.

353 Vicia sylvatica 'Wood Vetch'

A trailing plant with 1-2 m (3-6 ft) long stems bearing many-paired leaves, ending in tendrils. The flowers are white with mauve veins, in long-stalked racemes. Occurs on leaf mould in woods. Flowers July-August.

354 Oxalis acetosella
Wood-sorrel

A small plant, 5-15 cm (2-6 ins.) high, with trifoliate leaves and fairly large, white flowers veined with purple, on long slender stalks. Common on hedge-banks and in shady woods. Flowers April-May.

355 Geranium sanguineum
'Bloody Cranesbill'

A plant 15-45 cm (6-18 ins.) high with hairy stems, deeply palmate leaves and large purple flowers. Native and widespread over most of the British Isles but absent from S.E. England and Ireland. Flower April-May.

356 Geranium sylvaticum
'Wood Cranesbill'

A plant 30-50 cm (12-20 ins.) high with glandular hairs on the stems, 5-7-lobed leaves and large, reddish-purple flowers. Grows on leaf mould in woods, in meadows, and on rock ledges, absent from Wales. Flowers June-July.

357 Geranium pyrenaicum
'Mountain Cranesbill'

A plant 20-40 cm (8-16 ins.) tall with erect, hairy stems, palmately lobed leaves and mauve flowers in pairs in a loose cyme; the petals are twice as long as the sepals. Doubtfully native but common in southern England though rarer westwards and northwards. Flowers June-September.

358 Geranium robertianum
Herb Robert

A plant 15-40 cm (6-16 ins.) high, covered with soft, glandular hairs, and with reddish stems, leaves palmately divided and lobed, and rose pink flowers. Common in woods and hedgerows. A special form of this species may be found fairly frequently on stony or pebbly beaches. Flowers May-August.

359 Geranium lucidum
'Shining Cranesbill'

A slender plant with red, translucent stems, 10-30 cm (4-12 ins.) high, shiny, palmately-lobed leaves and small, rose-pink flowers. Native, on shady rocks and walls, locally common but rare in N. Scotland. Flowers June-August.

360 Geranium pusillum
'Small-flowered Cranesbill'

An annual with creeping or ascending stems, 15-30 cm (6-12 ins.) long, branching from the base, covered with dense, velvety hairs; the leaves are palmately lobed and the flowers small, pale mauve or white. Found on cultivated ground or waste places in England and Wales. Flowers June-August.

361 Geranium molle
'Dove's-foot Cranesbill'

Resembles the plant above but can be recognised by its stems, being covered with soft, spreading, unevenly long hairs, and by having slightly larger, rose-pink flowers. Common throughout British Isles. Flowers May-September.

361a Geranium dissectum
'Cut-leaved Cranesbill'

Resembles the previous 2 species, but differs in having more erect stems, 15-25 cm (6-10 ins.) high, and by the leaves which are divided to the base into very narrow lobes. The flowers are dark red. Fairly common throughout the British Isles, in fields and on roadsides. Flowers June-July.

362 Erodium cicutarium
Common Storksbill

A plant 10-30 cm (4-12 ins.) high with bipinnately divided leaves, rose-pink flowers in umbels and fruits with long beaks. Common on dry sandy fields and also on sea-shores and dunes. Flowers April-September.

363 Polygala vulgaris
Common Milkwort

A plant 10-20 cm (4-8 ins.) high with narrow leaves and terminal clusters of blue, white or pink flowers. Common in meadows and on grassy downs. Flowers June-August.

364 Linum catharticum
'Purging Flax'

A slender plant, 5-25 cm (2-10 ins.) high with forked stems and small white flowers. Common in meadows and on grassy downs, especially on chalk. Flowers June-August. *This plant is poisonous.*

365 Callitriche stagnalis
'Stagnant Water Starwort'

A pale green, water plant with 15-30 cm (6-12 ins.) long stems bearing narrow, spathulate, submerged leaves and ending in a rosette of floating leaves forming a star. The very inconspicuous flowers arise singly in the axils of the leaves. Common in ditches, ponds and streams. Flowers May-September.

366 Mercurialis perennis
Dog's Mercury

A plant 20-40 cm (8-16 ins.) high with opposite, elliptical, toothed leaves and small, green, unisexual flowers (the two sexes are on different plants). Common in woods and on shady mountain rocks. Flowers April-May.

The colour plate represents a shoot of a female plant with fruits.

367 Euphorbia peplus
'Petty Spurge'

An annual plant, 10-30 cm (4-12 ins.) tall with white, *poisonous milky juice*. The stem is branched and the leaves are ovate and entire. The very small, unisexual flowers are held in small, green cups, each containing a single, stalked female flower surrounded by numerous male flowers. Very common in cultivated or waste ground, a common weed in gardens. Flowers June-September.

368 Euphorbia helioscopia
'Sun Spurge'

Resembles the previous plant but differs in having a taller stem branching into an umbel, finely saw-toothed leaves and yellowish-green cup-shaped involucre. Common weed on cultivated soil. Flowers May-September.

369 Impatiens noli-tangere
Touch-me-not

An annual plant 30-60 cm (1-2 ft), with succulent, transparent stems, oval, round-toothed leaves, large yellow, irregular flowers in drooping, 2-4-flowered clusters and green pods which explode when the seed is ripe. Native, but very rare and local, by streams and on wet ground. Flowers June-August.

369a Impatiens parviflora
'Small Balsam'

Resembles the previous plant, but can be recognised by its serrated leaves and small, pale yellow flowers in erect clusters. Introduced, but naturalised in woods and waste places, mainly in S. and E. England. A weed in gardens. Flowers July-September.

370 Ilex aquifolium *Holly*

A shrub or small tree with stiff, glossy, evergreen leaves, the edges wavy and with spine-pointed teeth. Flowers small, white; fruits red. Native in woods and hedges throughout the British Isles and often planted in parks and gardens. Flowers in June.

371 Euonymus europaeus
Spindle-tree

A shrub or small tree with elliptical, finely serrate leaves and small, whitish-green flowers. The fruit is a four-lobed capsule, red with orange seeds. Fairly common in thickets and hedgerows, mostly on calcareous soils. Flowers May-June.

372 Acer campestre *Common Maple*

Shrub or small, deciduous tree with 3-5-lobed leaves and small, green flowers in erect corymbs. The fruit is a schizocarp, separating into 2, with wings spreading horizontally. Native; fairly common in woods and thickets in the southern parts of England; elsewhere planted in gardens. Flowers in May (after the leaves are out).

373 Acer pseudoplatanus *Sycamore*

A tall, deciduous tree with 5-lobed, toothed leaves, dark green above and pale bluish-grey or reddish underneath, and green flowers in hanging panicles. The fruits have wings set at oblique angles. Introduced in the 15th and 16th century and now common in woods and gardens. Flowers in May (after the leaves are out).

374 Acer platanoides *Norway Maple*

A moderate-sized tree with pointed, lobed leaves and yellowish-green flowers in erect panicles. The fruits have spreading wings. Introduced; but becoming naturalised. Flowers in May before the leaves.

375 Frangula alnus
Alder Buckthorn, Black Dogwood

A shrub with elliptical, entire leaves and small, whitish-green flowers. The fruits are red at first, then black. Common in damp woods and bogs. Flowers in June. *The fresh bark and the fruits are poisonous.*

376 Rhamnus cathartica *Buckthorn*

A shrub with alternate, densely thorny branches, finely serrate, elliptical leaves and small, green, unisexual flowers in clusters near the axils of the leaves (male and female flowers on distinct plants). The fruits remain green for some time but eventually turn black. Grows in hedges and woods on calcareous soils. Flowers May-June. *The fruits are poisonous.*

377 Tilia cordata
'Small-leaved Lime'

A tall tree up to 80 feet, with obliquely heart-shaped leaves, bluish-green beneath, with small, rust-coloured tufts of hair in the angles of the veins. The pale yellow flowers are in cymes with an oblong bract on the flower stalk. The fruits are nut-like; when ripe, the whole fruit falls off at once, together with the bract which acts like a wing. In woods, especially on limestone, in the southern parts of the country; sometimes planted in the north. Flowers in July.

377a Tilia vulgaris *Common Lime*

Resembles the previous tree, but differs in the leaves being a fresh green on both sides, and by having whitish tufts of hair in the angles of the veins on the under side of the leaves. Doubtfully native but planted on roadsides and in parks. Flowers in July.

378 Malva sylvestris
Common Mallow

An erect plant, 40-90 cm (2-3 ft) high,

5-7 lobed leaves and large, reddish-purple flowers. The fruit is a disc-shaped schizocarp. Common in the south, less common in the north along roadsides and on waste places. Flowers July-September.

379 Malva pusilla *'Small Mallow'*

An annual plant with 15-30 cm (6-12 ins.) long stems, decumbent or ascending, leaves lobed and very small, flowers white or pink with petals not much longer than the sepals. Introduced: found on waste places. Flowers June-August.

379a Malva neglecta
Dwarf Mallow

Resembles the foregoing plant but has larger flowers, whose pink petals are more than twice as long as the sepals. Native and grows in similar places, chiefly in the South. Flowers June-September.

380 Hypericum maculatum
'Imperforate St John's Wort'

A plant 30-50 cm (12-20 ins.) high, with a quadrangular stem, oval leaves and yellow flowers whose sepals are rounded at the tip. Common in damp places, in woods and pastures. Flowers July-August.

381 Hypericum perforatum
Common St John's Wort

Resembles the previous species, but has a 2-angled stem, narrower leaves and a wider corymb of yellow flowers with pointed sepals. Common, especially on calcareous soils. Flowers July-August.

382 Helianthemum oelandicum
'Oeland Rockrose'

A low, shrubby plant with oblong leaves and quite small, yellow flowers with slightly recurved petals. Common on the island of Oeland in Sweden but does not occur anywhere else in the world. Flowers in June.

383 Helianthemum nummularium
Rockrose

A low shrub, 10-30 cm (4-12 ins.) high with procumbent and ascending stems, oval leaves and large, yellow flowers. Common on grassland over most of England but absent from Cornwall and N. Scotland.

384 Drosera rotundifolia *Sundew*

An insectivorous plant with radical leaves in a rosette, fringed with stalked, stickly red hairs by means of which the plant catches and digests small insects. The little, white flowers are on bare stems 6-15 cm (2-6 ins.) high. Common in bogs and wet, peaty places on heaths and moors. Flowers July-August.

385 Viola hirta *'Hairy Violet'*

A tuft-forming plant with hairy radical leaves and bluish-purple, scentless flowers on 5-10 cm (2-4 ins.) high stems from the axils of the basal leaves. Fairly common on calcareous pastures and in woods. Flowers April-May.

386 Viola odorata *Sweet Violet*

Has long runners with rosettes of roundish, basal leaves and sweetly scented, bluish-purple flowers on 5-10 cm (2-4 ins.) stems, from the axils of the leaves. Native; common in hedge-banks and shady places, usually on calcareous soil. Flowers March-April.

387 Viola riviniana *'Common Violet'*

A plant 8-20 cm (3-8 ins.) high, having both radical leaf rosettes and ascending, leafy, flowering stems. The flowers are usually blue-violet with a thick, whitish spur and have no scent. Common in woods, on heaths and mountain rocks. Flowers April-May.

387a Viola sylvestris
'Pale Wood Violet'

Resembles the above plant but differs in having bluish-purple flowers with a pointed, purple spur. Grows in similar places but is less common. Flowers in May.

388 Viola canina
Heath Violet, Dog Violet

Resembles the Common Violet (No. 387) but is shorter and has no leaf rosettes at the base of the stems. Common in open woods, in hedge banks, on heaths and dry downs, usually on calcareous soils. Flowers May-June.

389 Viola palustris *'Marsh Violet'*

A plant with a creeping stem, 5-10 cm (2-4 ins.) long, smooth, rounded leaves and small, mauve flowers. Fairly common in bogs and wet meadows. Flowers in May.

390 Viola biflora *'Alpine Violet'*

A prostrate plant with stems 10-20 cm (4-8 ins.) long and rounded leaves and yellow flowers. Grows in gardens but not found wild in Great Britain. Flowers June-August.

391 Viola tricolor *Wild Pansy*

A plant 10-30 cm (4-12 ins.) tall, with oblong leaves which have large, lobed stipules. The flowers are quite large and their colour may vary; usually the 4 top petals are a bluish-violet and white whilst the lowest are yellow with black stripes; but the blue colour may be lacking as shown in the flower on the right. Common in poor, sandy fields and dunes. Flowers May-October. In gardens, improved large-flowered forms are grown.

392 Viola arvensis *'Field Pansy'*

Resembles the foregoing plant but can be recognised by the much smaller flowers, generally whitish-yellow. Common, especially on clay soils; also grown in gardens. Flowers May-October.

393 Myriophyllum spicatum
'Spiked Water-milfoil'

A water-plant with stems up to 3 ft in length, bearing whorls of finely pinnate, much divided leaves. The inconspicuous flowers are in whorls on a spike which rises above the water. Common in lakes and ponds. Flowers June-August.

394 Hippuris vulgaris *Mare's Tail*

A water plant with erect, 15-80 cm (6 ins.-3 ft) high stems, partly rising above the water and bearing dense whorls of narrow leaves with tiny inconspicuous flowers in their axils. Common in ditches and water-holes. Flowers June-August.

395 Hippophae rhamnoides
Sea Buckthorn

A much branched, thorny shrub with narrow leaves with a silvery sheen beneath, and orange fruits. The minute, yellowish-brown flowers appear before the leaves. Common on dunes and cliffs by the sea, from Yorkshire to Sussex.; planted elsewhere.

396 Daphne mezereum *Mezereon*

A low shrub with red, sweet-scented flowers, glabrous, oblong leaves and red, *poisonous berries*. Cultivated in gardens and also native in England from Yorkshire southwards, very local. Flowers March-April, before the leaves.

397 Lythrum salicaria
Purple Loosestrife

A bog plant, 0.5-1 m (19 ins.-3 ft) with narrow leaves and red flowers in a long, terminal spike. Common in bogs and fens, on the margins of lakes and slow rivers; locally abundant. Flowers July-August.

398 Circaea lutetiana
Common Enchanter's Nightshade

A plant 15-40 cm (6-16 ins.) tall, with ovate or cordate, faintly toothed leaves and small, white flowers. The nut-like fruits are covered with hooked bristles. Common on moist soil in shady woods. Flowers in August.

399 Epilobium montanum
Broad-leaved Willow-herb

A plant 30-50 cm (12-20 ins.) high, with a thick underground stem and with elliptical leaves and small, rose-pink flowers. The long, narrow pods contain small, light seeds with tufts of hairs. Common in woods and thickets. Flowers June-August.

400 Epilobium hirsutum
Great Hairy Willow-herb, Codlins and Cream

A robust plant, 80-150 cm (2-5 ft) high, with erect hairy stems, oblong leaves and large, rose-pink flowers. Common in bogs and reedy fens and on the margins of lakes and rivers. Flowers July-September.

401 Epilobium hornemannii
'Moss Willow-herb'

A slender plant, 8-30 cm (3-12 ins.) high with slightly toothed, elliptical leaves and small, reddish-purple flowers. Not native in the British Isles. Flowers July-August.

402 Epilobium palustre
Marsh Willow-herb

A plant 15-40 cm (6-16 ins.) with narrow leaves and small, pink flowers. Common in bogs and on the margins of lakes. Flowers July-August.

403 Epilobium anagallidifolium
'Alpine Willow-herb'

A slender plant, only 5-8 cm (2-3 ins.) high, with small, elliptical leaves and nodding, reddish-violet flowers. By streams on mountains from Yorkshire northwards. Flowers July-August.

404 Chamaenerion angustifolium
Rosebay Willow-herb, Fireweed

An erect plant, 50-125 cm (20 ins.-4 ft) high with narrow leaves and large, purplish-red flowers in a long, densely-flowered spike. Common in rocky places throughout the British Isles, but chiefly in the south. Flowers July-August.

405 Cornus suecica *'Dwarf Cornel'*

A plant 10-30 cm (4-12 ins.) high with ovate leaves and small, blackish-red flowers surrounded by 4 white, flower-like bracts. The berries are red. Grows on heather moors and in heath bogs; very local in England, more frequent in Scotland. Flowers May-June.

On the colour plate a flowering plant is shown on the left and a fruit-bearing plant on the right.

406 Cornus sanguinea *Dogwood*

A shrub with red branches, elliptical leaves, small, white flowers in umbel-like inflorescences, and blue-black fruits. Grows in woods on calcareous soils. Flowers June-July.

407 Hedera helix *Ivy*

An evergreen shrub which, by the aid of adhesive roots along the stem, can climb up trees or walls to a great height, but which often merely creeps along the ground. The leaves are palmately lobed (as shown on the left of the colour plate), except on the flowering shoots which have elliptical leaves (see picture on the right). The small, yellowish-green flowers are in round umbels. Common in woods and hedges and on rocks; also planted in gardens and at the foot of walls. Flowers September-October.

408 Eryngium maritimum
Sea Holly

A stiff, erect plant 25-50 cm high, branched, glabrous and glaucous blue with broad, spiney leaves and small, pale blue flowers in round heads. Grows on sandy shores and beaches. Flowers in July.

409 Hydrocotyle vulgaris
Pennywort, White-rot

A plant 5-20 cm (2-8 ins.) long, the stems creeping and bearing longstalked, shield-shaped leaves. The small, greenish flowers are in few-flowered heads on short, erect stalks. In bogs, fens and on the edges of lakes, usually in acid soils. Flowers July-September.

410 Sanicula europaea *Sanicle*

A plant 20-40 cm (8-16 ins.) high with long-stalked, palmately lobed, radical leaves and an almost leafless stem. The small white flowers are in tight heads, in a branching umbel. Common in woods. Flowers June-July.

411 Chaerophyllum temulum
'Rough Chervil'

A plant 30-80 cm (1-3 ft) high, with red, leaves bipinnately or tripinnately divided and umbels of white flowers, nodding in bud. Fairly common in woods and hedges. Flowers June-July.

412 Anthriscus sylvestris
Cow Parsley, Keck

A plant 50-120 cm (2-4 ft) high with hollow, grooved stems, hairy at the base; finely divided leaves; white many-flowered umbels and smooth, blackish-brown fruits about 5 mm (¼ ins.) long. Very common on roadsides, in waste places and the edges of woods. Flowers May-June.

413 Conium maculatum *Hemlock*

Resembles the previous plant, but

differs in having a thick, glabrous stem with a blue bloom and red spots and short, ribbed fruits. Grows in damp places, open woods and near water. Flowers May-June.

414 Myrrhis odorata *Sweet Cicely*

A soft-haired and sweetly scented plant, 50-100 cm (20-40 ins.) tall, resembling Cow Parsley (No. 412), but easily distinguished by its large, shining blackish-brown fruits, up to 2 cm (1 ins.) long. Doubtfully native; frequently found near inhabited places, escaped from earlier cultivation as a kitchen herb. Flowers June-July.

415 Cicuta virosa *Cowbane*

A fen plant, 50-120 cm (2-4 ft) with large white flowers in umbels and bipinnately or tripinnately divided leaves with narrow, acute teeth. Introduced; rather rare throughout the British Isles. Flowers July-August. *This plant is so poisonous as to be deadly.*

416 Carum carvi *Caraway*

A plant 25-60 cm (10-24 ins.) high with white or faintly reddish flowers in umbels, and finely divided leaves with very narrow segments. Introduced: naturalised in waste places throughout the British Isles. Flowers May-July.

417 Pimpinella saxifraga
     'Burnet Saxifrage'

Has a striped stem 15-30 cm (6-20 ins.) high, the leaves on the upper part being reduced to almost leafless sheaths, the lower ones being pinnately divided into ovate, serrate or deeply lobed segments. The flowers are white or reddish. Common in dry grassy places throughout the British Isles. Flowers July-August.

418 Torilis japonica
     'Upright Hedge-parsley'

A rough, greyish-green plant, 50-60 cm (20 ins.-2 ft) high with small pink or white flowers in umbels and bipinnate leaves. The fruits are studded with hooked bristles. Common in hedges and on grassy places. Flowers June-July.

419 Aegopodium podagraria
     Ground Elder, Goutweed, Herb Gerard

A plant 30-80 cm (12-32 ins.) high, with white, many-flowered umbels and ternate leaves with broad, saw-toothed segments. Probably introduced; at one time used as a pot-herb, now common in waste places near buildings or as a weed in gardens.

420 Angelica sylvestris
     Wild Angelica

A stout plant, 80-150 cm (2-5 ft) high, with a thick, hollow stem, glaucous blue or tinged with red on the upper part, and with large, twice or thrice pinnate leaves with broad serrated segments The white or reddish flowers are in large, flat umbels. Common in bogs, meadows and in moist woods. Flowers July-August.

421 Archangelica litoralis
     'Seashore Angelica'

Resembles the previous plant, but is even more robust and differs in having a completely glabrous stem and pale green flowers in arching umbels. Does not occur in the British Isles. Flowers July-August.

422 Heracleum sibericum
     'Siberian Cow Parsnip'

A robust, 80-150 cm (2-5 ft) high, rough-haired plant with pinnately divided leaves, the segments lobed and toothed. The numerous yellowish-green flowers are in large compound umbels, each of which consists of smaller arching umbels. Does not occur in the British Isles. Flowers June-July.

422a Heracleum sphondylium
Cow-parsnip, Hogweed

Resembles the foregoing species but differs in having white or reddish flowers, in flat umbels, the outer flowers much larger than the central ones. Native; common throughout the British Isles. Flowers June-July.

423 Laserpitium latifolium

A glabrous, blue-green plant, 80-150 cm (2-3 ft) tall, one of the many Umbelifers with large, white-flowered umbels and twice or thrice pinnate leaves, the segments rounded. Not found in the British Isles. Flowers July-August.

424 Pastinaca sativa *Wild Parsnip*

A robust plant with a straight, angular, grooved stem about 3 feet high, pinnately divided leaves and umbels of yellow flowers. Native; common on roadsides and in fields particularly on chalk. Flowers July-August.

425 Peucedanum palustre
Hog's Fennel, Milk Parsley

A plant 60-120 cm (2-4 ft) high with white-flowered umbels and twice or thrice pinnate leaves, the lobes small and narrow, ending in a fine point. Fairly common in bogs and marshes, chiefly in eastern England. Flowers July-August.

426 Sium latifolium *Water Parsnip*

A smooth, 50-150 cm (2-5 ft) tall bog plant with white-flowered umbels and pinnate leaves, the segments oblong and finely serrate. Rare, in fens and wet ground, chiefly in England and southern Scotland. Flowers July-August. *This plant is poisonous.*

427 Sium erectum
'Narrow-leaved Water Parsnip'

A smooth, 30-80 cm (1-3 ft) high bog plant with spreading branches and lateral, white-flowered umbels. The leaves are pinnate with toothed segments. Common in ditches, streams and brooks. Flowers July-August. *This plant is poisonous.*

428 Oenanthe fistulosa
Water Dropwort

A blue-green bog plant, 25-50 cm (10-20 ins.) high, with reddish-white flowers, hollow stems and leaf-stalks, and narrowly-lobed leaves. Native; in ponds and marshes; very rare in the north-west and absent from the south-west of the British Isles. Flowers July-August. *This plant is poisonous.*

429 Oenanthe aquatica
'Fine-leaved Water Dropwort'

A bog plant 50-100 cm (20-40 ins.) tall, with a thick, hollow, curved branched stem, white-flowered umbels and finely divided leaves. Local, in slow-flowing or stagnant water. Flowers July-August. *This plant is poisonous.*

430 Aethusa cynapium
Fool's Parsley

A plant 30-60 cm (1-2 ft) high, with a glabrous and glaucous stem, purplish-red at the base, and shiney, twice or thrice pinnate leaves with narrowly lobed segments. The white flowers are in umbels, each of which has 3 narrow, drooping, one-sided bracts. Native but also a common weed in gardens and fields. Flowers June-September. *This plant is poisonous.*

431 Daucus carota *Wild Carrot*

A plant 30-60 cm (1-2 ft) high, the stem covered with stiff hairs, and finely divided leaves with narrowly-lobed segments. The umbels have white flowers, with an occasional red flower in the centre, surrounded at their base by large, lobed bracts. After the flowers have faded, the stems bend upwards and inwards (see picture on the left). Common on roadsides, in fields, on chalky soil and near the sea. Flowers July-August.

The Wild Carrot has a thin, tough root as opposed to the cultivated form.

432 Pyrola secunda
'Serrated Wintergreen'

A plant 10-20 cm (4-8 ins.) high with elliptical leaves and small greenish-white flowers in a nodding raceme. Native in woods on damp rock ledges, chiefly in the north west. Flowers in July.

433 Pyrola uniflora
'One-flowered Wintergreen'

A low plant with roundish leaves and solitary, nodding, white flowers at the end of the 5-15 cm (2-6 ins.) long stems. Native in pinewoods, very local in eastern Scotland. Flowers June-July.

434 Pyrola rotundifolia
'Larger Wintergreen'

A plant 10-30 cm (4-12 ins.) high with long-stalked, rounded radical leaves and a terminal cluster of quite large, white flowers with spreading petals and a long, curved style. Native; in bogs and on damp ledges; very local, chiefly found in eastern districts. Flowers June-July.

435 Pyrola minor
'Common Wintergreen'

A plant 10-30 cm (4-12 ins.) high, with oval radical leaves and almost globular, reddish-white flowers, the short, straight style is hidden among the petals. Native; in woods, on moors in England; rather local in Scotland. Flowers in July. ·

436 Monotropa hypopitys
Yellow Bird's Nest

A yellowish, saprophytic plant without chlorophyll. The succulent, 10-20 cm (4-8 ins.) tall stem is densely covered with scales and ends in a cluster of yellow, bellshaped flowers, nodding at first, then erect. Native, but rather local, in woods particularly beech or pine. Flowers June-July.

437 Rhodondendron lapponicum
'Arctic Rhododendron'

A low, evergreen, dwarf shrub with small, oval leaves and erect, reddish-violet flowers. Grows in the Scandinavian mountains and in Greenland, but not in the British Isles. Flowers in June.

438 Ledum palustre
'Marsh Ledum'

A low shrub with narrow, evergreen leaves, rusty brown underneath, and umbels of numerous, white flowers. Rare and perhaps native in Stirlingshire and Perthshire. Flowers June-July.

439 Loiseleuria decumbens
'Loiseleuria'

A decumbent, evergreen, dwarf shrub with oval leaves and small pink flowers. Native; on mountain tops and moors at high altitudes, from Stirling and Dumbarton northwards. Flowers June-July.

440 Phyllodoce coerulea
'Blue Phyllodoce'

A low, evergreen, dwarf shrub with needle-shaped leaves and nodding, bottle-shaped flowers, reddish-purple at first, becoming bluish later. Native on rocky mountains, very rare. Flowers in June.

441 Cassiope hypnoides

A tender, moss-like, everygreen, dwarf shrub with soft, needle-like leaves and white, nodding flowers. Does not occur in the British Isles. Flowers July-August.

442 Cassiope tetragona

A 10-30 cm (4-12 ins.) high, evergreen, dwarf shrub with small, densely clustered leaves in 4 rows, and white, nodding flowers. Not native in the British Isles. Flowers in July.

443 Andromeda polifolia
Marsh Andromeda

An evergreen shrub, 15-30 cm (6-12 ins.) tall with narrow leaves, whitish-grey underneath, and pink, nodding flowers. Native, in bogs but very local. Flowers June-July.

444 Arctostaphylos alpina
'Black Bearberry'

A low, deciduous, dwarf shrub with serrate leaves, small, white flowers and blackish-red fruits. Native; on mountain moors, very local. Flowers May-June.

445 Arctostaphylos uva-ursi
Bearberry

A prostrate, evergeen, dwarf shrub with entire leaves, pink, bottle-shaped flowers and red fruits with floury flesh. Native on high moors; local. Flowers May-June.

446 Oxycoccus palustris
Cranberry

A slender, evergreen, dwarf bush with creeping, thread-like stems, oval leaves, rose-pink flowers on erect stems, and red berries. Grows in peat bogs or on wet heaths, local. Flowers June-July.

447 Vaccinium vitis-idaea
Cowberry, Red Whortleberry

A dwarf shrub 5-20 cm (2-8 ins.) high with evergreen leaves, glossy and dark green on the upper surface but lighter and spotted below. The pink or white flowers are in nodding racemes and have bell-shaped corollas. The berries are red. Grows on moors and in woods on acid soils. Flowers in June.

448 Vaccinium uliginosum
'Bog Whortleberry'

A 10-70 cm (4-28 ins.) high, deciduous shrub with stout, brown branches, simple leaves and nodding, white or pink flowers. The berries are blue. Grows in moist moorland bogs and on dunes. Native, from Durham and Cumberland northwards, rare elsewhere. Flowers May-June.

449 Vaccinium myrtillus
Billberry, Blaeberry, Whortleberry

A deciduous, dwarf shrub, 15-40 cm (6-16 ins.) high, with green, angular branches, finely toothed leaves and nodding, white or reddish flowers with an almost globular corolla. The berries are blue with reddish-purple juice. Common throughout most of the British Isles, on heaths and moors. Flowers in May.

450 Calluna vulgaris
Ling, Heather

A 15-50 cm (6-20 ins.) tall, evergreen shrub with small, needle-like leaves and reddish purple (less often white) flowers in dense clusters. Common on heaths, moors and bogs throughout the British Isles. Flowers July-September.

451 Erica tetralix
Cross-leaved Heath, Bog Heather

A 10-30 cm (4-12 ins.) tall, dwarf, evergreen shrub with whorls of needle-shaped leaves and nodding, rose-pink (more rarely white) flowers with a globose corolla. Common on damp moors, in heaths and mountain bogs. Flowers July-August.

452 Empetrum nigrum *Crowberry*

A low, evergreen, dwarf shrub with procumbent branches, densely crowded, needle-shaped leaves, inconspicuous red flowers and black fruits. The flowers are unisexual and the male and female flowers grow on distinct plants. Grows on moors and in heath bogs. Common in Scotland, N. England and Wales, rarer in the South. Flowers in April.

On the colour plate a twig of a female plant with ripe fruits can be seen on the left and a shoot of a flowering male plant on the right.

453 Diapensia lapponica

A low plant forming dense tufts, with narrow, leathery leaves and quite large, white flowers. Does not occur in the British Isles but is sometimes grown in gardens. Flowers June-July.

454 Androsace septentrionalis
'Mountain Pimpernel'

A slender plant, 5-15 cm (2-6 ins.) high, with whorls of basal leaves and leafless stems bearing umbels of small, white flowers. Does not occur in the British Isles but grown in gardens. Flowers May-June.

455 Primula vulgaris *Primrose*

A plant 10-20 cm (4-8 ins.) high with leaves in a basal rosette and large, pale yellow flowers, singly on long stalks. Common in woods and hedges; common throughout the British Isles, less common in the north. Flowers April-May.

456 Primula elatior *Oxlip, Paigle*

A plant 15-30 cm (6-12 ins.) high, with elliptical leaves in a basal rosette and flowers in a one-sided umbel at the top of the flower stem. The corolla is tubular at the base, the lobes spreading, and paler yellow than the throat. In woods and on chalk downs; grows chiefly in south-eastern England. Flowers April-May.

457 Primula farinosa
'Bird's-eye Primrose'

A slender plant, 10-25 cm (4-10 ins.) high with basal leaves mealy white underneath and a crowded umbel of reddish-mauve flowers. Grows in moist meadows; chiefly found in northern England and southern Scotland. Flowers May-June.

458 Primula veris *Cowslip, Paigle*

A plant 10-30 cm (4-9 ins.) high, with crinkled, downy-haired, basal leaves and umbels of yellow flowers, the corolla being tubular below, the lobes wide-spread above with 5 orange spots in the throat. Common on grassy downs and in meadows; rarer in the north. Flowers May-June.

459 Hottonia palustris
Water Violet

A water-plant with deeply pinnatifid, submerged leaves and pale lilac flowers in a whorl, raised above the water on 15-30 cm (6-12 ins.) high, leafless stems. In ditches and ponds in England and Wales, rather local elsewhere. Flowers May-June.

460 Lysimachia vulgaris
Yellow Loosestrife

A plant 40-90 cm (16 ins.-3 ft) high, with elliptical leaves and yellow flowers in a large, terminal spike. In fens and beside rivers, locally common but absent from N. Scotland. Flowers June-August.

461 Lysimachia nummularia
Creeping Jenny

A prostrate plant with stems 10-40 cm (4-16 ins.) long, bearing circular or oval leaves in two rows and large, yellow flowers in the axils of the leaves. Grows in moist hedgerows and grassy places; common in England, rarer and perhaps an escape from cultivation in the north. Flowers June-July.

462 Lysimachia thyrsiflora
'Tufted Loosestrife'

A bog-plant 25-60 cm (10-24 ins.) high, with oblong leaves and small yellow flowers in dense, axillary racemes. Native but rare, in wet marshes and ditches. Flowers June-July.

463 Trientalis europaea
Chickweed Wintergreen

A slender plant, 5-15 cm (2-6 ins.) tall, with elliptical leaves in a whorl at the top of the stem and one or two white, star-shaped flowers at the top. In pine woods, rare in southern England, commoner from Yorkshire northwards. Flowers June-July.

464 Glaux maritima
'Sea Milkwort', Black Saltwort

A low, glabrous, succulent plant having 5-20 cm (2-8 ins.) long, decumbent or ascending stems, with oblong leaves and small, rose-pink flowers in the axils of the leaves Locally common on salt marshes. Flowers June-July

465 Anagallis arvensis
Scarlet Pimpernel, Shepherd's Weather-Glass

A small decumbent plant with 5-30 cm (2-12 ins.) long stems, oval leaves and red flowers which only open in the middle of the day, Common by roadsides and on cultivated land. Flowers June-August.

466 Armeria maritima
Trift, Sea Pink

A plant, 10-30 cm (4-12 ins.) high with basal rosettes of narrow leaves and rose-pink flowers in heads, surrounded by membraneous bracts. Common on salt marshes; may also be found in sandy pastures inland. Flowers May September.

467 Limonium humile
'Lax-flowered Sea Lavender'

A plant, 10-30 cm (4-12 ins.) high, with oblong, radical leaves and a branched inflorescence of bluish-violet flowers with scarious calyx. Common on salt marshes in England. Flowers July-September.

468 Gentiana nivalis
'Small Gentian'

A plant 5-15 cm (2-6 ins.) high with ovate leaves and flowers of a deep blue; the petals spreading above the throat. Native but local; on rock ledges in the mountains of Perth and Angus. Flowers June-August.

469 Gentiana pneumonanthe
'Marsh Gentian'

A plant 10-30 cm (4-12 ins.) high, with narrow leaves and blue, bell-shaped flowers, striped with green on the outside. On wet heaths from Dorset to Cumberland, very local; rare elsewhere.

470 Gentiana campestris
'Field Gentian'

A plant 5-30 cm (2-12 ins.) high, with oblong leaves and purplish-blue flowers with a fringe in the throat of the corolla. Grows on grassy downs and pastures; common in Scotland and N. England but absent from S.E. England. Flowers June-September.

471 Centaurium minus
Common Centaury

An annual plant, 10-40 cm (4-16 ins.) high, with rose-pink flowers in dense clusters at the top of the branching stem. The leaves are oval, and the tube of the corolla is twice as long as the calyx. On dry grassland; common in England and Ireland, less so in Scotland. Flowers July-August.

472 Centaurium vulgare
'Sea Centaury'

Resembles the previous species, but differs in having narrower leaves and somewhat larger, dark red flowers, whose calyx is of the same length as the tube of the corolla. Sandy places near the sea, rather local. Flowers July-August.

472a Centaurium pulchellum
'Small Centaury'

An annual plant, 2-25 cm (1-10 ins.) high, differing from the 2 previous species in having the stem branched from the base and no basal rosette of leaves. Damp grassy places, often near the sea; rather local. Flowers July-October.

473 Menyanthes trifoliata
Buckbean, Bogbean

A robust aquatic bog plant with creeping stems over 3 ft in length, and 3-foliate leaves on erect stalks. The flowers are in a raceme on 10-40 cm (4-16 ins.) high stalks; corollas are reddish on the outside, but white and fringed inside. Rather common in the British Isles in ponds and on the edges of lakes. Flowers May-June.

474 Cynanchum vincetoxicum

A tall plant, 30-70 cm (12-28 ins.) high, with pointed, heart-shaped leaves and small, yellowish-white flowers in racemes in the axils of the leaves. The seeds have a tuft of white hairs. Not native in the British Isles. Flowers June-July. *The plant contains a poisonous milky juice.*

475 Fraxinus excelsior *Ash*

A tall tree with opposite, unequally pinnate leaves and oblong, winged fruits in hanging bunches. The flowers are small, without petals but the stamens are purplish black and held several together in panicles; the stalks lengthen as the fruits ripen. Native and forming woods on calcareous soils; sometimes planted in parks and gardens. Flowers April-May (before the leaves appear).

On the colour plate is shown a twig with leaves and unripe fruits at the top, and below, a flowering twig.

476 Convolvulus sepium
Bellbine, Larger Bindweed

Has twining stems, 1-3 m (3-10 ft) long, arrow-shaped leaves and large, white, funnel-shaped flowers with two heart-shaped bracts at the base. Common in hedges, especially in Southern England. Flowers June-July.

477 Convolvulus arvensis
Bindweed, Cornbine

Has creeping or twining stems, 20-75 cm (8-30 ins.) long, arrow-shaped leaves and white or pink flowers with a funnel-shaped corolla. Common in fields and waste places, in England and Wales but rarer in Scotland. Flowers June-September.

478 Cuscuta europaea
Large Dodder

A leafless, parasitic plant with thread-like, reddish stems twining round plants and bushes, sucking nourishment from these by means of suckers. Small reddish flowers in dense heads. Grows chiefly in southern England, very rare in Scotland. Most frequently parasitic on the Stinging Nettle. Flowers June-August.

479 Polemonium caeruleum
Jacob's Ladder

A plant 30-60 cm (1-2 ft) high, having unequally pinnate leaves and large blue flowers. Native; local, on limestone hills in N. England. Grown in gardens and sometimes found as a garden escape. Flowers July-August.

480 Asperugo procumbens
Madwort

A stiff-haired plant with decumbent stems 15-60 cm (6 ins.-2 ft) long and oblong leaves. The flowers are small and dark purple; the calyx grows during the ripening of the fruit into a toothed, compressed covering round the fruits. Introduced and found in waste places or near houses. Flowers May-July.

481 Lithospermum arvense
'Corn Gromwell', 'Bastard Alkanet'

An annual plant, 15-40 cm (6-16 ins.) high, with narrow leaves, small white flowers and greyish-brown, wrinkled fruits. Native in England in arable fields; rare and perhaps not native in the rest of the British Isles. Flowers May-June.

482 Myosotis palustris
'Water Forget-me-not'

A decumbent or erect plant, 15-40 cm (6-16 ins.), with oblong leaves and fairly large flowers of a beautiful sky-blue (red before they open), with a yellow throat. The calyx is 5-toothed and covered with flattened hairs. Common in wet meadows and ditches. Flowers June-August.

482a Myosotis laxa
'Water Forget-me-not'

Resembles the previous species and, like it, has a calyx with flattened hairs, but differs in having smaller flowers and a more deeply lobed calyx (cleft to the middle). Grows in similar places and is fairly common but occurs more frequently in mountain districts. Flowers June-August.

482b Myosotis sylvatica
'Wood Forget-me-not'

Resembles *M. palustris* (No. 482) and has flowers of the same size as that species, but can easily be recognised by its calyx being deeply lobed and covered with spreading, hooked hairs. Grows in damp woods, locally throughout Great Britain, rarer in the north. Improved forms are cultivated in gardens. Flowers May-June.

483 Myosotis versicolor
Yellow and Blue Forget-me-not

A slender, hairy plant, 8-25 cm (3-10 ins.) high with small, short-stalked flowers, yellow at first, afterwards bluish-violet. Locally common in grassy places throughout the British Isles. Flowers May-June.

484 Myosotis arvensis
'Common Forget-me-not

A plant 15-40 cm (6-16 ins.) high, with small, blue flowers whose stalks, after the flower has faded, lengthen considerably, up to three times as long as the calyx. Common in fields and in woods. Flowers May-June.

485 Myosotis stricta
'Early Forget-me-not'

A small plant, 5-15 cm (2-6 ins.) high with tiny flowers on very short, erect stems. Common in sandy fields and on downs. Flowers April-May.

485a Myosotis hispida
'Early Forget-me-not'

Resembles the species above, but differs in the flowers which are on slightly longer stalks that spread out after the flowers have faded. Common in similar places. Flowers April-May.

486 Echium vulgare
Viper's Bugloss

A straight, stiff-haired, annual, 30-90

cm (1-3 ft) high with oblong leaves and funnel-shaped, blue flowers (red before opening). Common in dry fields, on downs and roadsides throughout the British Isles. Flowers June-July.

487 Symphytum officinalis
Comfrey

A stiff-haired plant with 40-100 cm (16-40 ins.) high stems which are winged by the decurrent bases of the large, oblong leaves. The flowers are nodding with a bell-shaped, lilac, rose-pink or whitish-yellow corolla. Common along the sides of streams and in wet meadows throughout Great Britain, but less common in the north and possibly not a native there. Flowers June-August.

487a Symphytum asperum
'Rough Comfrey'

Resembles the previous plant, but differs in having broader leaves, the edges decurrent. Introduced; an escape from earlier cultivation as a fodder plant. Flowers June-September.

488 Mertensia maritima
'Northern Shore-wort'

A glaucous, decumbent plant with 20-50 cm (8-20 ins.) long stems, oval leaves and small, light blue flowers. Native on shingle beaches; very rare in the south, local in the north. Flowers June-July.

489 Anchusa arvensis *Bugloss*

A 15-40 cm (6-16 ins.) tall, stiff-haired plant with oblong, curved leaves and sky-blue flowers with a curved tube to the corolla. On sandy and chalky soil, locally common in Great Britain. Flowers May-July.

490 Anchusa officinalis *Alkanet*

A tall, rough-haired plant, 30-60 cm (1-2 ft) high, with oblong leaves and

flowers of a dark bluish-purple (red before opening), the throats white. Probably introduced; on sandy fields and roadsides, very local. Flowers June-July.

491 Cynoglossum officinale
Hound's-tongue

A soft-haired plant, 30-80 cm (1-nearly 3 ft) high, with oblong leaves, brownish-red flowers and flat, prickly fruits. Widely distributed in grassy places on dry soil near the sea; more local in the north. Flowers May-June.

492 Pulmonaria officinalis
Lungwort

A 10-30 cm (4-12 ins.) high plant with oblong stem leaves and flowers, red at first, afterwards bluish-purple, with a funnel-shaped corolla. The radical leaves are heart-shaped. Introduced; naturalised in woods, mainly in southern England. Flowers April-May.

493 Ajuga reptans *Bugle*

An almost glabrous plant, 10-30 cm (4-12 ins.) tall, with runners and oval leaves. The small, blue flowers are in a terminal spike surrounded by bracts tinged with violet. Common in woods and damp meadows throughout the British Isles. Flowers May-June.

494 Ajuga pyramidalis
Pyramidal Bugle

Differs from the previous species by having no runners, by its dense covering of woolly hairs, and in having larger floral leaves of a stronger colour, among the flowers. Very local on limestone rocks, especially in the north. Flowers May-June.

495 Scutellaria galericulata
Skull-cap

A plant 30-60 cm (1-2 ft) high with quite narrow leaves and blue flowers, in pairs in the axils of the leaves. Common in fens, on the edges of streams and in wet meadows. Flowers July-August.

496 Prunella vulgaris *Self-heal*

A plant 5-25 cm (2-10 ins.) high, with oval leaves and a short, terminal spike of bluish-purple flowers. Common in grassland and open woods. Flowers July-September.

497 Galeopsis tetrahit
'Common Hemp-nettle'

A plant 20-70 cm (8-28 ins.) high, with a hispid, quadrangular stem, inflated below the nodes of the leaves. The leaves are oval and serrate, and the flowers are mauve-red (rarely white). Common in fields, less often in woods and fens. Flowers July-September.

498 Galeopsis ladanum
Red Hemp-nettle

A downy-haired plant, 10-30 cm (4-12 ins.) high, with oblong, serrate leaves and rose-pink flowers with a yellow spot on the lower lip. Introduced; rare, in waste and cultivated ground. Flowers July-August.

499 Galeopsis speciosa
'Large-flowered Hemp-nettle'

A stiff-haired plant, 30-90 cm (1-3 ft) high, with serrate, elliptical leaves and large, yellow flowers with a purple lower lip. Native, but rather local in wet fields. Flowers July-September.

500 Lamium album
White Dead-nettle

A plant, 25-60 cm (10 ins.-2 ft) high, with coarsely toothed leaves resembling those of the nettle. But without the stinging hairs, and with large, white, labiate flowers in whorls in the axils of the leaves. Common along roadsides and in waste places. Flowers May-August.

501 Lamium galeobdolon
Yellow Archangel

The plant has both long, decumbent, winter shoots with green leaves and erect, 15-30 cm (6 ins.-1 ft) high flowering shoots. The leaves are ovate and toothed and often have white spots on the upper side (especially on the winter shoots). The flowers are large and yellow. Grows in woods, usually on heavy soil; rare in Scotland. Flowers May-June.

502 Lamium amplexicaule *Henbit*

A 10-25 cm (4-10 ins.) high plant bearing kidney-shaped, palmately lobed leaves and red flowers with straight tubes to the corollas. A common weed on light, dry soils. Flowers May-August.

503 Lamium purpureum
Red Dead-nettle

A plant 15-30 cm (6 ins.-1 ft) high, with toothed, heart-shaped leaves and red flowers. Very common on cultivated ground. Flowers April-October.

504 Glechoma hederacea
Ground Ivy

This plant has long, decumbent stems as well as erect ones, 10-20 cm (4-8 ins.) high, which bear the flowers. The leaves are kidney-shaped and with rounded teeth, the flowers are purple. Small female flowers often occur. Common in woods and waste places, usually on damp, heavy soil. Flowers April-June.

505 Thymus serpyllum
Wild Thyme

A low evergreen plant with creeping stems which send up erect, 3-10 cm (1-4 ins.) high flowering shoots, which have almost tubular stems, hairy all round. The leaves are narrowly ovate and the flowers are a reddish-mauve (rarely white). Fairly common on dry grassland and heaths. Flowers July-August.

505a Thymus pulegioides
'Larger Wild Thyme'

Resembles the previous plant but is more robust and is recognised by its broader leaves and sharply quadrangular stem which is hairy only on the edges. The whorls of flowers are spaced out up the stem. Native; common on dry downs and pastures, rarer in the north and absent from Scotland. Flowers July-August.

506 Origanum vulgare *Marjoram*

A plant 30-50 cm (12-20 ins.) high with ovate leaves and a panicle of small flowers of a pale lilac colour, in dense, oval heads, surrounded by reddish-purple bracts. In dry pastures usually on calcareous soils; common in England and Wales, local in Scotland. Flowers July-September.

507 Leonurus cardiaca
Motherwort

A plant, 50-100 cm (20-40 ins.) high, with lower leaves palmately lobed and the upper ones 3-lobed. The small, red flowers are in axillary whorls. Introduced; rare but found in waste places in various parts of the British Isles. Flowers July-August.

508 Stachys sylvatica
'Hedge Woundwort'

A 40-100 cm (16-40 ins.) high, dark green, downy plant with broad, coarsely toothed leaves and flowers of a dark brownish-red with white veins on the lower lip. Common in woods and shady places. Flowers July-August.

509 Stachys palustris
'Marsh Woundwort'

A plant 25-70 cm (10-28 ins.) high with narrow leaves and rose-pink flowers with white veins. Common in woods and waste places throughout the British Isles. Flowers July-August.

510 Ballota nigra
Black Horehound

A plant 40-90 cm (16 ins.-3 ft) high, with broad, wrinkled, coarsely toothed leaves and purple flowers with white veins. Common on roadsides and banks in England and Wales, rarer in Scotland. Flowers July-September.

511 Clinopodium vulgare
Wild Basil

A softly hairy plant, 20-50 cm (8-20 ins.) high, with ovate leaves and red flowers surrounded by bristly bracts. Common in hedges and scrub on calcareous soil in England, more local in the North. Flowers July-August.

512 Calamintha acinos
Basil-thyme

A plant 10-30 cm (4 ins.-1 ft) high with small, oval leaves. The flowers are bluish-violet with a white spot on the lower lip. Grows in dry fields, rather local especially in the north. Flowers June-August.

513 Lycopus europaeus *Gipsy-wort*

A bog plant, 25-70 cm (10-28 ins.) high, with coarsely-toothed leaves and small white flowers with red spots, in dense whorls in the axils of the leaves. Common in England on the banks of lakes and streams. Flowers July-August.

514 Mentha arvensis *'Corn Mint'*

Has creeping or ascending stems, 10-30 cm (4 ins.-1 ft) long, ovate leaves and small, purple flowers in whorls in the axils of the leaves. Common, especially in arable fields and damp places. Flowers July-September.

515 Mentha aquatica '*Water Mint*'

Has an upright stem, 25-80 cm (10-32 ins.) high, ovate leaves and small, purple flowers in a terminal head. Strong smell of mint. Common in marshes, on the margins of lakes and in bogs. Flowers July-September.

516 Solanum nigrum
'*Black Nightshade*'

A plant 10-40 cm (8-16 ins.) high with toothed, ovate leaves, white flowers and black berries. A weed in gardens and on waste places throughout England, becoming rarer in Scotland. Flowers July-October.

517 Solanum dulcamara
Bittersweet, Woody Nightshade

A twining, woody plant, up to 2 m (7 ft) high, with spear-shaped leaves, purple flowers and oblong, red berries. Common in woods and on waste ground in England, absent from Scotland. Flowers June-July. *This plant is poisonous.*

518 Hyoscyamus niger *Henbane*

A plant 25-70 cm (10-28 ins.) high, with viscid, glandular-hairy stems and entire or toothed leaves; the flowers are a yellow colour with purple veins. The fruit is a capsule surrounded by the bottle-shaped calyx. Grows in sandy places, especially near the sea; widely scattered throughout the British Isles. Flowers June-August. *This plant is highly poisonous.*

At the top of the colour plate can be seen the upper part of a flowering plant and below it a couple of ripe fruits.

519 Lycium halimifolium
Duke of Argyll's Tea-plant

A low shrub with spreading, hanging branches, somewhat spiney, narrow leaves, reddish-mauve flowers and oblong, red berries. Introduced but often planted in hedges. Flowers June-August.

520 Verbascum nigrum
'*Dark Mullein*'

A plant 30-100 cm (1- over 3 ft) high with broad leaves, darkgreen above and woolly-grey below. The flowers are in terminal racemes, yellow with purple spots, the filaments are clothed with purple hairs. Native; on cultivated ground from Cumberland southwards. Flowers July-August.

521 Verbascum thapsus
Aaron's Rod

A tall plant, 0.4-1.5 m (16 ins.-5 ft) high, clothed in soft whitish wool, with oblong leaves and a long spike of yellow flowers, 1.5-2.5 cm (¾-1 ins.) across, and hairy or smooth stamens. Fairly common on sunny banks in dry soil; rare in Scotland. Flowers July-August.

521a Verbascum thapsiformis
'*Great Mullein*'

Resembles the previous species but differs in having flowers twice as large, 3-5 cm (1-2 ins.). Grows in similar places and sometimes found as a casual. Flowers July-September.

522 Digitalis purpurea *Foxglove*

A plant 50-150 cm (20 ins.-5 ft) high, with oblong leaves and a long one-sided raceme of large, nodding flowers with a red, bell-shaped corolla. Common in woods and on heaths; native and found throughout the British Isles. Flowers June-August. *This plant is very poisonous.*

523 Scrophularia nodosa *Figwort*

Has a quadrangular stem, 50-100 cm (20-40 ins.) high, broad, serrate leaves and a large panicle of small, brownish-green flowers. Common in damp woods and hedges throughout the British Isles. Flowers June-August.

524 Linaria minor
'*Small Toadflax*'

A much branched annual, 10-20 cm (4-8 ins.) high, with hairy stems bearing narrow leaves and small, purple flowers with a pale yellow lip and a short spur. Common in grassy places and hedgerows in England and southern Scotland. Flowers July-August.

525 Linaria vulgaris *Toadflax*

A plant, 15-50 cm (6-20 ins.) high, with narrow, bluish-green leaves and a long, dense raceme of large, yellow flowers with an orange blotch and a long spur. Common in cultivated fields and hedgebanks, in England and Southern Scotland. Flowers July-September.

526 Veronica spicata
'*Spiked Speedwell*'

A plant 20-30 cm (8-12 ins.) high with oblong leaves and a long, densely flowered spike of bluish-mauve flowers. Grows in dry grassland in East Anglia but rare although a native. Flowers July-August.

527 Veronica arvensis
'*Wall Speedwell*'

An annual with stems 5-25 cm (2-10 ins.) high, bearing oval, round-toothed leaves and ending in a long raceme of small blue flowers in the axils of narrow leaves. Common throughout the British Isles, on cultivated ground and heaths. Flowers April-June.

528 Veronica persica
'*Buxbaum's Speedwell*'

A creeping plant with 10-30 cm (4-12 ins.) long stems bearing small, toothed leaves. The flowers are on long stalks in the axils of the leaves; the large corolla is sky-blue, the lower lobe white. The capsules are broader than long. Introduced about 1825, now common on cultivated land throughout the British Isles. Flowers April-May and August-October.

529 Veronica hederifolia
'*Ivy Speedwell*'

A decumbent annual plant with 10-30 cm (4-12 ins.) long stems, 3-5-lobed leaves and small flowers, pale mauve in colour, on thin stalks from the axils of the leaves. Common on cultivated land throughout the British Isles. Flowers April-May.

530 Veronica alpina
'*Alpine Speedwell*'

A creeping plant, 5-15 cm (2-6 ins.) long, with oval leaves and small, dark blue flowers in a dense head at the end of the stem. Native, on damp alpine rocks in N. Scotland. Flowers June-August.

531 Veronica verna
'*Spring Speedwell*'

An erect annual with stems 5-15 cm (2-6 ins.) high, bearing lobed leaves and ending in clusters of minute, blue flowers in the axils of the narrow, upper leaves. Native but local; in dry grassland in East Anglia. Flowers April-May.

532 Veronica agrestis
'*Field Speedwell*'

Resembles *V. persicaria* (no. 528), but differs in having considerably smaller flowers, whitish at first, later becoming pale blue with reddish stripes; only the lower segment of the corolla remains white. Capsules slightly inflated. Native and found on cultivated ground throughout the British Isles. Flowers in May and August-September.

532a Veronica opaca
'Procumbent Speedwell'

Resembles the previous species but differs in having denser hairs and tiny, entirely blue flowers with a white tube to the corolla. Found in cultivated fields. Flower April-May and August-September.

533 Veronica chamaedrys
'Germander Speedwell'

Has prostrate stems, 10-30 cm (4-12 ins.) long which have 2 lines of hairs down their length and ovate, toothed leaves. The quite large flowers of a pretty, sky-blue colour, are in clusters from the axils of the leaves. Common in meadows, hedges and woods. Flowers May-July.

534 Veronica serpyllifolia
'Thyme-leaved Speedwell'

A plant with prostrate stems, 10-25 cm (4-10 ins.) long, erect when flowering, with glabrous, oval leaves and small, bluish-white flowers in terminal racemes. Common throughout the British Isles on heaths and waste places. Flowers May-June.

535 Veronica beccabunga
Brooklime

A smooth, fleshy, bog plant with 15-50 cm (6-20 ins.) long, creeping stems and oval leaves and small, dark blue flowers in racemes from the axils of the leaves. Common in streams, marshes and wet meadows. Flowers July-August.

535a Veronica anagallis-aquatica
'Water Speedwell'

Resembles the foregoing species but differs in having smaller, saw-toothed leaves and flowers of a pale blue colour in longer racemes. Fairly common in similar places. Flowers June-August.

536 Veronica officinalis
'Common Speedwell'

Has 10-25 cm (4-10 ins.) long stems, creeping and rooting, often forming mats, with hairy, elliptical leaves and upright spikes of small, bluish-purple flowers. Common in grassland, woods, heaths and dry fields. Flowers June-July.

537 Veronica scutellata
'Marsh Speedwell'

A 10-30 cm (4-12 ins.) long, bog plant with creeping stems, becoming erect, narrow leaves and small reddish or bluish-white flowers in few-flowered, leafy spikes. Grows in ponds, bogs and wet meadows; common throughout the British Isles. Flowers May-July.

538 Odontites rubra *'Red Bartsia'*

A plant 10-40 cm (4-16 ins.) high with narrow, distantly toothed leaves and long, one-sided spikes of red flowers in the axils of the small, red leaves. Common in fields throughout the British Isles. Flowers June-September.

539 Euphrasia officinalis
Eyebright

A small plant, 5-40 cm (2-16 ins.) high, with oval, toothed leaves and dense spikes of white and mauve flowers with darker stripes and a yellow spot on the lip. Common in meadows and pastures. Flowers June-September.

540 Melampyrum pratense
'Common Cow-wheat'

An annual plant, 10-30 cm (4-12 ins.) high, with narrow leaves and pale yellow flowers in pairs in the axils of the leaf-like bracts. Common in woods and on moors. Flowers June-August.

541 Melampyrum sylvaticum
'Wood Cow-wheat'

Resembles the foregoing species, but differs in having golden yellow flowers with a shorter corolla, only slightly longer than the sepals. Grows in woods at high altitudes, very local. Flowers July-August.

542 Melampyrum nemorosum
'Florest Glade Cow-wheat'

A 20-50 cm (8-20 ins.) high plant with oblong leaves and golden yellow flowers, surrounded by purple, toothed bracts. Grows in woods and thickets; local.

543 Melampyrum cristatum
'Crested Cow-wheat'

An annual, 15-30 cm (6-12 ins.) high with narrow, toothed leaves and 4-sided spikes of purple flowers with yellow lips, surrounded by reddish-purple bracts. Very local, at the edges of woods. Flowers June-August.

544 Rhinanthus serotinus
Greater Yellow-rattle

A plant, 25-40 cm (10-12 ins.) high with narrow, toothed leaves and dense spikes of yellow flowers with a curved tube to the corolla and an inflated, yellowish-green calyx. In cornfields and meadows in Scotland and N. England; rare in the south. Flowers May-August.

545 Rhinanthus minor
Yellow-rattle

Resembles the previous plant, but is more slender and differs in the flowers having straight tubes to the corolla and a calyx tinged with brown. Common in pastures and on heaths. Flowers May-June.

546 Bartsia alpina
'Alpine Bartsia'

A plant 20-30 cm (8-12 ins.) high, with leaves tinged with brownish-purple and flowers of the same colour. In high places on rock ledges from Yorkshire

northwards. Flowers June-August.

547 Pedicularis palustris
Red-rattle

An annual plant, 25-40 cm (10-16 ins.) high, with pinnately divided leaves and clusters of purple-red flowers which have an inflated, 2-lobed calyx, with a crinkled edge. Common in meadows and wet heaths. Flowers May-August.

548 Pedicularis sylvatica
Lousewort

Resembles the above species, but can be recognised by the 2-5-toothed calyx and by the upper lip of the flowers being longer than the lower lip. Common in marshes and wet pastures. Flowers May-June.

549 Pedicularis sceptrum-carolinum *'Royal Sceptre Lousewort'*

A plant 30-90 cm (1-3 ft) high, with pinnately lobed leaves and large, yellow flowers which never open. Grows in meadows. Not found in the British Isles. Flowers July-August.

550 Pedicularis lapponica
'Lapland Lousewort'

A plant 5-25 cm (2-10 ins.) high with pinnately divided leaves and yellowish-white flowers in a tight head. Not found in the British Isles. Flowers July-August.

551 Pedicularis oederi
'Oeder's Lousewort'

A 10-20 cm (4-8 ins.) high plant with pinnately lobed leaves and a dense cluster of yellow flowers with a dark brown spot on the tip of the upper lip. Not found in the British Isles Flowers June-August.

552 Lathraea squamaria

A leafless parasite, the rootstock densely covered with thick, white scales. Only the 10-20 cm (4-8 ins.) high flowering shoots appear above ground; these are flesh-coloured and end in a one-sided raceme of nodding, pink flowers. Locally common on the roots of plants, especially Elm and Hazel in limestone areas. Flowers April-May.

553 Utricularia vulgaris
'Greater Bladderwort'

A floating water-plant without roots, but with very finely divided submerged leaves, the thread-like segments bearing bladders that catch small insects which are digested by the plant which is carnivorous. The yellow 2-lipped flowers are raised above the water on stems 20-50 cm (8-10 ins.) long. Local throughout the British Isles, usually in relatively deep water. Flowers July-August.

554 Pinguicula vulgaris
Common Butterwort

An insect-eating plant with a basal rosette of oval leaves with inrolled edges and a greasy, shiny surface covered with a sticky slime in which insects and other small animals are caught. The flowers are violet with a 2-lipped corolla; they are solitary on 6-20 cm (2-8 ins.) long stems. Common on wet heaths and in bogs. Flowers May-July.

555 Plantago major
'Great Plantain'

A plant 10-40 cm (4-16 ins.) high with broad leaves in a rosette and a long spike of small brownish flowers with a membraneous corolla. Common in fields, on roadsides and near houses. Flowers June-August.

556 Plantago maritima
'Sea Plantain'

A perennial plant, 10-30 cm high, with succulent, linear leaves and a narrow spike of small flowers with conspicuous, yellow stamens. Common in salt marshes around the coast and in the mountains. Flowers July-September.

557 Plantago lanceolata
'Ribwort'

A 10-40 cm (4-16 ins.) high plant with lanceolate leaves and comparatively short, thick brown, flower spikes with yellowish-white stamens. Common in grassy places and by roadsides. Flowers May-July.

558 Plantago media
'Hoary Plantain'

A plant 15-40 cm (6-16 ins.) high, with oval, downy leaves and fairly thick flower spikes with conspicuous, lilac stamens. Common on grassy downs and roadsides in S. England and the Midlands, rarer northwards. Flowers May-July.

559 Plantago coronopus
Buck's-horn Plantain

A small plant, only 3-15 cm (1-6 ins.) high, with pinnately lobed leaves covered with grey hairs, and short flower spikes. Common on sandy soils near the sea, throughout the British Isles. Flowers July-August.

560 Littorella uniflora *Shore-weed*

A small plant, 3-8 cm (1-3 ins.) in height, with narrow leaves in a rosette and small, unisexual flowers. The male flowers are held singly on short, erect stalks; the female flowers 2-3 together at the base of the stalks of the male flowers. Grows in dense colonies in shallow water or on shores of lakes and ponds. Fairly common in England in suitable habitats but commoner in the north. Flowers June-July.

On the colour plate, a flowering plant which has grown on the exposed margin of a lake is shown on the left, and on the right 2 sterile plants with runners which have grown under water.

561 Sherardia arvensis
Field Madder

A small, decumbent plant with stems 5-15 cm (2-6 ins.) long, leaves in whorls and small, blue flowers in terminal heads. Common in arable fields and waste places. Flowers June-August.

562 Asperula odorata
Sweet Woodruff

A perennial plant, 10-30 cm (4-12 ins.) high, with whorls of lanceolate leaves and small, white flowers in terminal cymes. Locally abundant in the British Isles, in woods on damp soils. Flowers May-June.

563 Galium boreale
'Northern Bedstraw'

Has stiffly upright stems, 15-50 cm (6-20 ins.) high, bearing whorls of 4 leaves with 3 veins each and ending in a branched panicle of small, white flowers. Grows on rocky slopes, scree and shingle, locally common in the British Isles. Flowers July-August.

564 Galium saxatile
'Heath Bedstraw'

Has 5-25 cm (2-10 ins.) long, decumbent or a scending stems, ovate leaves in whorls of 4-6, and small, white flowers in terminal panicles. Common on heaths, moors and in woods on acid soils throughout the British Isles. Flowers June-July.

565 Galium palustre
'Marsh Bedstraw'

A slender plant with stems 15-60 cm (6 ins.-2 ft) high, ascending or decumbent, and whorls of generally 4 narrow leaves of unequal length, with rounded tips. White flowers in a loose panicle. Common in marshes, fens and along streams throughout the British Isles. Flowers June-August.

565a Galium uliginosum
'Fen Bedstraw'

Resembles the previous species, but differs in having narrow leaves ending in spiney points, in whorls of 6. Grows in similar localities. Flowers June-August.

566 Gallium mollugo
'Great Hedge Bedstraw'

Has weak stems 25-80 cm (10-32 ins.) long, ascending or erect, glabrous, with narrow leaves in whorls of 6-8, and small, white flowers in a large, spreading panicle. Common on hedgebanks, scrub and grassy slopes in the south. Flowers July-August.

567 Galium verum
Lady's Bedstraw

A plant, 10-60 cm (4 ins.-2 ft) high with whorls of generally 8 very narrow leaves with rolled-back edges. The small, yellow flowers in a terminal, leayf panicle. On grassland and sandy dunes; very common in the British Isles. Flowers June-August.

568 Galium aparine
Goose Grass, Cleavers

Has much branched, rough, brittle, creeping or climbing stems, up to more than 3 ft in length, and inconspicuous flowers of a dirty white colour. The fruits are covered with hooked bristles and readily adhere to anything that touches them. Very common throughout the British Isles in hedges and waste places. Flowers June-September. On the colour plate, the tip of the fruit-bearing plant is shown on the left, a flowering shoot on the right.

569 Lonicera periclymenum
Honeysuckle

A shrub whose thin, pliant stems climb up and over other plants. The large, pale yellow or pink flowers are in dense heads at the tips of the shoots. The berries are red. Common in woods and hedges Flowers July-August.

570 Lonicera xylosteum
Fly Honeysuckle

An upright, much branched shrub with downy-haired leaves and small whitish-yellow flowers, 2 together in the axils of the leaves. The red berries are in pairs. Probably native, in woods and hedges in Sussex; in other places in the British Isles, probably introduced. Flowers May-June.

571 Sambucus nigra *Elder*

A shrub or small tree with unequally pinnate leaves and small, yellowish-white flowers in flat umbels. The fruits are blackish-purple. The branches have a white, spongy pith. Native and common throughout the British Isles in woods and waste places; also planted in gardens. Flowers June-July.

572 Sambucus racemosa
'Grape Elder'

Resembles the previous species in habit, but differs in having yellow pith and small, yellowish-green flowers in a dense panicle. The fruits are red. Introduced and commonly planted but is also becoming naturalised. Flowers April-May.

573 Viburnum opulus
Guelder Rose

A shrub with 3-5-lobed leaves and flat cymes with large, barren, white flowers in the centre. Fruits red. Fairly common in woods and hedges on damp soils. Flowers in June.

574 Adoxa moschatellina
Moschatel, Townhall Clock

A tender, pale green herb, 5-15 cm (2-6 ins.) in height, with thin, palmately divided leaves and small, green flowers in a terminal head. Native, in woods but rather local. Flowers April-May.

575 Linnaea borealis *'Linnaea'*

A slender prostrate plant with evergreen leaves and nodding, reddish-white flowers, in pairs on 5-15 cm (2-6 ins.) high, erect shoots. Grows in woods, especially pine forests; extinct in England, local and rare in Scotland. Flowers June-July.

576 Valerianella locusta
Lamb's Lettuce, Corn Salad

A slender, pale green plant, 5-25 cm (2-10 ins.) in height, with oblong leaves and small, densely packed, pale blue flowers. Grows on arable land, dunes, dry fields; common throughout the British Isles. Flowers in May.

577 Valeriana dioica
'Marsh Valerian'

An erect plant, 10-30 cm (4-12 ins.) high, with ovate, radical leaves and pinnate stem leaves. The small, pink and white flowers are unisexual and dioecious (i.e. the two sexes are on different plants). In marshy meadows and bogs, throughout Great Britain. Flowers May-June.

On the colour plate is shown a flowering male plant. The female plants have smaller and more densely packed flowers.

578 Valeriana sambucifolia
'Elder-eaved Valerian'

An 0.5-1 m (20-40 ins.) tall plant with pinnate, toothed leaves and small, pink or white, bisexual flowers in many-flowered corymbs. Common in bogs and ditches. Flowers June-July.

579 Succisa pratensis
Devil's-bit Scabious

A 25-60 cm (10 ins.-2 ft) high, downy
haired plant with oblong leaves and
blue flowers in almost globular heads.
Common in meadows and pastures and
in damp woods. Flowers August to
September.

580 Scabiosa columbaria
'Small Scabious'

An erect plant 25-50 cm (10-20 ins.)
high, branching, with pinnate basal
leaves and finely divided stem leaves.
The flowers are purple with a 5-lobed
corolla; held in hemispherical heads,
the marginal flowers being the largest.
Grows on dry, chalky slopes and
pastures; locally common in the British
Isles. Flowers July-September.
The colour plate shows the top of a
flowering plant and a leaf from the
lower part of the stem.

581 Knautia arvensis
'Field Scabious'

A 30-50 cm (12-20 ins.) high, stiff-
haired plant with oblong, coarsely
toothed, radical leaves and pinnate
stem leaves. The flowers are a reddish
mauve, with a 4-lobed corolla, in
hemispherical heads, the marginal
flowers being the largest. Common on
dry fields and banks, in England and
Wales, less common in the north.
The colour plate shows the top of a
flowering plant and a leaf from the
lower part of the stem.

582 Campanula persicifolia
'Narrow-leaved Campanula'

An erect, 30-70 cm (12-28 ins.) high
plant with narrow leaves and bell-
shaped flowers, blue in colour. Introduced but well established now in
the south-western counties and re-

corded elsewhere in England and
Scotland. Flowers June-July.

583 Campanula latifolia
Large Campanula

A plant 60-120 cm (2-4 ft) high with a
smooth and slightly hairy, saw-toothed
leaves. The lower leaves are broadly
ovate, the upper ones narrower. The
large bluish-purple flowers have spreading tips to the petals. Native in woods
and hedgebanks but commonest in the
north, local in England. Flowers
July-August.

584 Campanula trachelium
Bats-in-the-Belfry

A stiff-haired plant, 60-90 cm (2-3 ft)
high, with coarsely toothed leaves. The
lower leaves are heart-shaped, the
upper narrower. The flowers are a
dark purplish blue, the tips of the
petals spreading. In woods and hedgebanks on clay soil; rather local. Flowers
July-August.

585 Campanula rapunculoides
'Creeping Campanula'

A 30-60 cm (1-2 ft) high plant with a
long, one-sided raceme of nodding,
violet flowers with narrow, recurving
tips to the petals. Introduced and well
established in the south-western counties. Flowers July-September.

586 Campanula patula
Spreading Campanula

A glabrous plant, 25-60 cm (10 ins.-2
ft) high, with narrow leaves and
purple flowers, the petals spreading.
Native in shady woods, local throughout England and Wales. Flowers July-
August.

587 Campanula glomerata
Clustered Bellflower

A downy-haired plant, 25-60 cm (10
ins.-2 ft) high, with ovate leaves and

densely clustered, purple flowers. Native in grassy places on calcareous soils; locally common from Dorset to Kincardine. Flowers July-August.

588 Campanula rotundifolia
Harebell, Bluebell (of Scotland)

A slender plant, 10-45 cm (4-18 ins.) high, erect, branched stems and nodding blue flowers. The stem leaves are quite narrow, the radical leaves are long-stalked and kidney-shaped, with roundly toothed edges. Common throughout the British Isles in dry grassy places. Flowers July-August.
On the colour plate the radical leaves of the plant can be seen on the left, a flowering stem on the right.

589 Jasione montana
Sheep's Bit

An erect plant, 10-40 cm (4-16 ins.) high with narrow, stiff-haired leaves and small, pale blue flowers in terminal, round heads. Native but generally local in grassy places on light, sandy soils. Flowers June-August.

590 Lobelia dortmanna
'Water Lobelia'

A water plant, 15-40 cm (6-16 ins.) high, with narrow, basal leaves. The small, bluish flowers are raised above the surface of the water in a slim, terminal raceme. Native; in lakes and tarns with acid water. Locally common in Wales, the Lake District and Scotland. Flowers July-September.

591 Eupatorium cannabinum
Hemp Agrimony

A large plant, 50-150 cm (20 ins.-5 ft) high, with 3-5-lobed leaves, and a large corymbose inflorescence of small, pink flower-heads. A plant of marshes and fens throughout Great Britain but rarer in Scotland. Flowers July-September.

592 Aster tripolium *'Sea Aster'*

A glabrous plant, 15-60 cm (6 ins.-2 ft), high with narrow, fleshy leaves and a terminal inflorescence of showy flower-heads with purple ray-florets and yellow disk florets. Fairly common in salt marshes; a native but mostly found in estuaries in N. England and Scotland. Flowers August-October.

593 Solidago virgaurea
Golden-rod

An erect plant, 10-80 cm (4-32 ins.) high with oblong leaves and termi-nating in a branched inflorescence of small, golden yellow flowers. Common in dry woods, grassland and dunes throughout the British Isles, rarer in the South-East. Flowers July-October.

594 Erigeron acre
'Blue Fleabane'

A 10-40 cm (4-16 ins.) high, stiff-haired plant with narrow leaves and small, downy grey heads with filiform purple ray florets and yellow diks florets. Locally common in dry grass-land and sand dunes in England and Wales but rarer in Scotland. Flowers July-August.

595 Erigeron canadense
'Canadian Fleabane'

An annual plant, 10-80 cm (4-32 ins.) high with narrow leaves and a much branched inflorescence of tiny, greenish, flower-heads, the ray florets short and of a yellowish-white colour. Introduced; a local weed on waste ground in England and Wales, rare in Scotland. Flowers July-August.

596 Erigeron uniflorum
Alpine Fleabane

A plant, 5-15 cm (2-6 ins.) high, with narrow leaves and a terminal fairly large panicle with ray florets which are white at first, becoming purple, and yellow disc florets. Doubtfully occurring in the Hebrides. Flowers July-August.

597 Bellis perennis *Daisy*

A low plant with a rosette of basal leaves and 5-15 cm (2-6 ins.) high flower stems, each ending in a single head with white ray florets (occasionally red) and yellow disc florets. Common in grassy fields and meadows and on roadsides. Flowers March-November.

598 Filago minima
'Slender Cudweed'

A slender, downy plant, 6-15 cm (2-6 ins.) high, with small, pointed leaves and tiny, densely clustered flower-heads, the bracts brown and scarious at the tip. Common on dry sandy fields and downs but rare in the extreme north. Flowers July-August.

599 Filago arvensis
'Field Cudweed'

An annual plant, 10-30 cm (4-12 ins.) high, downy-white with narrow leaves and small flower-heads in dense clusters at the top of the branches. The flowers are pale yellow and inconspicuous. Introduced; a casual in dry, sandy fields and on heaths. Flowers July-August.

600 Antennaria dioica
Cat's-foot, Cat's-ear, Mountain Everlasting

This plant has creeping and rooting runners with tongue-shaped leaves, green on the top, downy white underneath, and erect shoots, 5-20 cm (2-8 ins.) high, with narrow leaves and ending in a dense corymb of white or, sometimes, pink heads. The flowers are unisexual and the 2 sexes are on separate plants. The heads of the male plants are round (as shown on the colour plate on the left), while the heads of the female plants are oblong (colour plate, right). Common on moors and dry downs. Flowers May-June.

601 Antennaria alpina
'Alpine Cat's-foot'

A small plant, 5-15 cm (2-6 ins.) high with narrow leaves and brownish flowers-heads. Not found in the British Isles. Flowers June-September.

602 Gnaphalium uliginosum
'Marsh Cudweed'

A cottony-grey plant, 5-20 cm (2-8 ins.) high, branched from the base, with narrow leaves. The small, pale brown flower-heads are clustered at the tips of the branches in dense corymbs, over-topped by the leaves at their base. Common throughout the British Isles in damp fields and heaths, on acid soil. Flowers July-August.

603 Gnaphalium sylvaticum
'Wood Cudweed'

A straight plant, 20-50 cm (8-20 ins.) high, with narrow leaves and small brown flower-heads in a long, narrow spike. Common on sandy ground in forest clearings, on roadsides and in fields. Flowers July-August.

604 Gnaphalium norvegicum
'Highland Cudweed'

Resembles the previous species but has a more compact spike of flower-heads. Native, but occurs only on alpine rocks in the mountains of Scotland. Flowers July-August.

605 Gnaphalium supinum
'Dwarf Cudweed'

A dwarf plant, 3-10 cm (1-4 ins.) high, with narrow leaves and a few dark-brown flower-heads at the top of the stem. Native on the Scottish mountains. Flowers July-August.

606 Gnaphalium arenarium
'Sand Cudweed'

A 15-30 cm (6 ins. - 1 ft) high, cottony grey plant with narrow leaves and a dense, terminal cluster of round, yellow flower-heads with shining bracts. Not native in the British Isles. Flowers July-September.

607 Inula salicina
'Willow-leaved Inula'

An almost glabrous plant, 25-50 cm (10-20 ins.) in height, with narrow spreading leaves and large, yellow flower-heads with long ray florets. Native but very rare; found only in Ireland. Flowers July-August.

607a Inula britannica
'British Inula'

Resembles the previous species, but differs in having white, cottony stems and broader, soft-haired leaves. Introduced in 1894 to Leicester, but may now be extinct. Flowers July-September.

608 Bidens cernuus
'Nodding Bur-Marigold'

A pale green plant, 15-60 cm (6 ins.-2 ft) in height, having oblong, toothed leaves and yellow, nodding flower-heads with disc florets only, although sometimes yellow ray florets may also be present. The seeds have 2-4 thorny bristles, which make them adhere to passers-by. Common in ponds and stream sides; locally distributed in the British Isles. Flowers August-September.

609 Bidens tripartitus
'Tripartite Bur-Marigold'

An annual plant, 15-60 cm (6 ins.-2 ft) high with lobed, dark-green leaves and upright, yellow flower-heads. Common in the mud on the edges of lakes and ponds, locally abundant. Flowers July-September.

610 Galinsoga parviflora
Gallant Soldier, Joey Hooker

An annual plant, 20-40 cm (8-16 ins.) high, with glabrous stems, slightly toothed, ovate leaves and numerous small flower-heads with short, white ray-florets and yellow disc-florets. Introduced; established as a weed in gardens and fields in S. England. Flowers July-October.

610a Galinsoga ciliata

Resembles the previous species, but differs in having hairy stems, toothed leaves and blackish-red glandular hairs on the upper branches of the stem. Grows in similar places but is not quite so common. Flowers July-October.

611 Anthemis arvensis
Corn Chamomile

A much-branched annual, 15-40 cm (6-16 ins.) high with flattened hairs, finely divided leaves and comparatively large flower-heads, which have white ray florets and yellow disk florets. There are scarious bracts among the flowers. Native, locally common in waste places and on arable land. Flowers June-August.

612 Anthemis tinctoria
Yellow Chamomile

An erect plant, 25-60 cm (10 ins.-2 ft) high, with finely divided leaves and large, yellow flower-heads. Introduced; a garden plant naturalised in Bucks and occurring now in many English and some Scottish counties.

613 Achillea ptarmica
Sneezewort

A plant, 25-60 cm (10 ins.-2 ft) high, with narrow, finely toothed leaves. The flower-heads are in lax corymbs; they have white ray-florets and yellow disk florets. Fairly common in wet meadows and marshes. Also occurs as a weed in wet fields. Flowers July-August.

614 Alchillea millefolium
Yarrow, Milfoil

A strongly scented plant, 15-50 cm (6-20 ins.) high, with very finely divided leaves and a dense corymb of tiny flower-heads with white, more rarely pink ray florets and yellow disk florets. Common in fields, on roadsides and in pastures. Flowers July-September.

615 Chrysanthemum segetum
Corn Marigold

A glabrous, glaucous plant, 15-40 cm (6-16 ins.) high, with coarsely toothed, oblong leaves and large, yellow flower-heads. Probably introduced, a common weed, especially on poor, acid soils. Flowers June-September.

616 Chrysanthemum leucanthemum *Marguerite, Moon Daisy, Ox-eye Daisy*

A plant 20-50 cm (8-20 ins.) high with oblong, toothed leaves and large single flower-heads with white ray florets and yellow disk florets. Common plant on grassland where the soil is good. Flowers June-July.

617 Tanacetum vulgare *Tansy*

An erect plant, 50-100 cm (20-40 ins.) in height, with a spicy scent, pinnate leaves and a dense corymb of yellow, button-shaped flowerheads without ray florets. Common on roadsides and along field boundaries throughout the British Isles. Flowers July-September.

618 Matricaria maritima
Scentless Mayweed

An erect or decumbent plant, 20-60 cm (8 ins.-2 ft) high, the finely divided leaves with filiform lobes. The flowerheads are large and have white ray florets, yellow disk florets and a receptacle filled with pith (cf. No. 620). A common weed; abundant throughout the British Isles; there are related forms occuring on sea-shores. Flowers June-October.

619 Matricaria matricarioides
'Pineapple Weed,' 'Rayless Mayweed'

An annual plant, 10-25 cm (4-10 ins.) high, with finely divided leaves and yellowish-green flower heads, containing tubular disk florets only, the ray florets absent. Introduced; a very common weed of waste places and waysides throughout the British Isles. Flowers July-September.

620 Matricaria chamomilla
Wild Chamomile

Resembles *M. maritima* (No. 618), but differs in its spicy scent and in having slightly smaller flower-heads, with a hollow receptacle. Native; locally abundant as a weed on cultivated soil and on waste places. Flowers June-October.

621 Artemisia campestris
'Field Southernwood'

A tuft-forming plant with thin, ascending stems, 30-60 cm (1-2 ft) in height, finely divided leaves and minute, nodding flower-heads in a much branched, one-sided panicle. Native but very local on the heaths of East Anglia. Flowers July-September.

622 Artemisia vulgaris *Mugwort*

A tall plant, 60-120 cm (2-4 ft) high, with narrowly lobed leaves dark green above and cottony white beneath. The small, cottony flower-heads form large, oblong panicles and have reddish-brown or pale yellow flowers. Common in waste places and hedge-rows. Flowers July-September.

623 Artemisia maritima
'Sea Wormwood'

A plant 15-60 cm (6 ins.-2 ft) high,

covered with white down, with finely divided leaves and ovoid flower-heads with reddish-yellow flowers. The plant is highly aromatic. Fairly common on the drier parts of salt marshes. Flowers August-September.

624 Artemisia absinthium
Wormwood

A tall plant, 50-100 cm (20-40 ins.), covered with greyish down and with a strong aromatic odour, deeply lobed leaves and nodding, hemispherical flower-heads of yellow florets. Native; fairly common in moist places throughout Great Britain. Flowers July-August.

625 Tussilago farfara *Coltsfoot*

Has 10-20 cm (4-8 ins.) high, scaly flower-stalks appearing before the leaves and bearing single, yellow flower-heads with numerous, thread-like ray florets and tubular disk florets. The leaves are broad, with angular-toothed margins, and covered with white felt underneath. Common in fields and waste places on clay slopes. Flowers March-April.

626 Petasites hybridus
Butterbur

The plant has 15-40 cm (6-16 ins.) high stems bearing red scales and ending in a cluster of red-flowered heads. The flowers appear before the long-stalked leaves, which may reach almost 2 ft. across. Native; common in wet meadows and by streams. Flowers April-May.

627 Petasites frigidus
'*Winter Butterbur*'

A mountain plant with 10-30 cm (4-12 ins.) high stems with reddish or yellowish-white flower-heads developing before the triangular leaves, lobed at the edges and with white

down underneath. Not found in the British Isles. Flowers June-July.

628 Senecio sylvaticus
'*Wood Groundsel*'

An annual plant, 30-70 cm (12-28 ins.) high, with pinnately lobed leaves and small yellow flower-heads with the outer florets recurved, held in a terminal, flat-topped corymb. Common in salt marshes. Flowers August-September.

629 Senecio vernalis
'*Spring Senecio*'

A 15-40 cm (6-16 ins.) high plant covered in loose white cotton and with wavy, pinnately lobed leaves and fairly large, pale yellow flowerheads with spreading, ligulate, outer florets. Does not occur in the British Isles. Flowers May-June and September.

630 Senecio viscosus
Stinking Groundsel

An annual plant, 15-40 cm (6-16 ins.) high, with viscous hairs, pinnately lobed leaves and yellow flower-heads with outer florets at first spreading, later rolled back. Probably native on waste ground, locally common. Flowers July-October. *This plant is poisonous.*

631 Senecio vulgaris *Groundsel*

A 6-30 cm (2 ins.-1 ft) high plant with pinnatifid leaves and small, yellow flower-heads normally consisting of disk florets only, the ray-florets absent. Native; on cultivated ground, abundant throughout the British Isles. *This plant is poisonous.*

632 Senecio jacobaea *Ragwort*

A tall plant, 30-100 cm (1- over 3 ft), having pinnately divided leaves and a dense corymb of fairly large, golden yellow flower-heads with spreading, ligulate ray florets. Native; a weed on waste places and pastures throughout the British Isles. Flowers July-September. *This plant is poisonous.*

633 Arnica montana
'*Mountain Arnica*'

A plant 20-40 cm (8-16 ins.) high, with large, oval radical leaves, sticky haired stems and large, yellow flower-heads with ligulate ray florets. Not found in Great Britain. Flowers June-July. *This plant is poisonous.*

634 Arctium tomentosum
'*Cottony Burdock*'

A robust plant, 60-120 cm (2-4 ft) high, with large, broad leaves with grey down below, and round flower-heads densely covered with white cottony down, with dark-red, tubular florets and bracts hooked and curved at the tip. Not native in the British Isles. Flowers July-August.

634a Arctium lappa
Great Burdock

Differs from the previous plant in having smooth bracts to the involucre, with long, hooked tips. Native, in waste places and waysides; local. Flowers July-September.

634b Arctium vulgare
'*Common Burdock*'

Resembles the previous 2 species, but differs in having arching, spreading side branches and large, 3-5 cm (1-2 ins.) broad flower-heads tinged with red and with rose-pink florets and only slightly felted bracts with spreading, hooked points. Native and common on waste places and in woods. Flowers July-September.

635 Arctium minus
Lesser Burdock

A 40-80 cm (16-32 ins.) tall, grey-green plant which differs from other Bur-docks in having relatively small flower-heads, $1^1/_2$-$2^1/_2$ cm ($^3/_8$-1 ins.) broad, with pink flowers and only slightly cottony bracts. Common on roadsides and waste places. Flowers July-August.

636 Carlina vulgaris
Carline Thistle

A stiff plant, 25-30 cm (10-20 ins.) high, bearing spiney-toothed leaves and large flower-heads with reddish-yellow florets and straw-coloured bracts resembling outer florets. Common on chalky downs in Great Britain. Flowers July-August.

637 Carduus crispus
'*Welted Thistle*'

A plant, 60-150 cm (2-5 ins.) high, with a spiney-winged stem, oblong, toothed and lobed leaves, finely spiney round the margins and white, cottony beneath. The heads have red, tubular florets and bracts with spiney points. The fruits have a hairy pappus, whereas all the following thistle species (Nos. 638-643) have a feathery pappus. Common on roadsides and in open woods, more frequent in the south than in the north. Flowers June-September.

638 Cirsium acaule
'*Stemless Thistle*'

A low plant with a rosette of pinnately-lobed, spiney leaves, in the centre of which is a single, short-stalked head of red-purple florets. Locally common in England, on dry downs and pastures, especially on chalk. Flowers July-August.

639 Cirsium vulgare
'*Spear Thistle*'

A robust plant, 40-100 cm (16-40 ins.) high, with a prickly-winged stem and pinnately lobed leaves with stiff, straw-coloured prickles. The large, red-purple flower-heads have spreading bracts with prickly points. Common on roadsides, waste places and in grassy fields, throughout the British Isles. Flowers July-September.

640 Cirsium palustre
'Marsh Thistle'

An erect plant, 80-150 cm (3-5 ft) high, with a reddish-brown, prickly-winged stem, branching only towards the top where the comparatively small, red-purple flower-heads are held in dense clusters. The leaves are pinnatifid and have quite weak prickles. Common throughout the British Isles in bogs and wet meadows. Flowers July-August.

641 Cirsium arvense
Creeping Thistle

A creeping plant with erect flowering shoots, 50-100 cm (20-40 ins.) high, bearing pinnately lobed, prickly-toothed leaves and large flower-heads in terminal clusters with reddish-mauve florets. The florets are unisexual and the 2 sexes grow on different plants. The male plants have globular flowering heads (see colour plate, left), and the female plants have oblong flower-heads (see colour plate, right). Native and very common in the British Isles; a troublesome weed on cultivated land. Flowers July-August.

642 Cirsium heterophyllum
'Melancholy Thistle'

A plant, 40-100 cm (16-40 ins.) high, with an unbranched stem ending in a single, large crimson-purple flower-head. The leaves are covered with silvery-white felt underneath; the upper and lower leaves are entire, the middle ones are pinnate. Grows in hilly pastures and open woodland, chiefly in the northern counties. Flowers June-July.

643 Cirsium oleraceum
'Cabbage Thistle'

A pale green, almost glabrous plant, 50-150 cm (20 ins.-5 ft) high, with large, pale yellow (rarely reddish) flower-heads. The leaves have weak, soft prickles on their edges. Introduced; established in a few localities in fens and ditches in England and Scotland.

644 Saussurea alpina
'Alpine Saussurea'

A rosette plant with a flowering stem 5-40 cm (2-16 ins.) high, with oblong leaves, grey underneath; the stem terminates in a corymb of reddish-purple flower-heads. Native on cliffs in Scotland and North Wales. Flowers July-September.

645 Serratula tinctoria *Saw-wort*

A 50-70 cm (20-28 ins.) high plant with sharply toothed leaves and dark red flower-heads in a branched corymb. Grows in meadows and edges of woods; local in England, Wales and southern Scotland. Flowers July-August.

646 Centaurea cyanus
Cornflower, Bluebottle

An annual plant, 40-60 cm (16 ins.-2 ft) high, with narrow, cottony leaves and pretty, blue flower-heads on long stalks. Fairly common in cornfields but becoming rarer. Flowers June-July.

647 Centaurea scabiosa
'Greater Knapweed'

A plant with an erect stem, 30-80 cm (12-32 ins.) high, with pinnatifid leaves and large, reddish-purple flower-heads, the bracts bordered with black fringing hairs. Common on dry grassland, hedgebanks and cliffs; common in the south, rarer in Scotland.

648 Centaurea jacea
'Brown-rayed Knapweed'

An erect plant, 20-70 cm (8-28 ins.) high, with narrow leaves and purplish-red flower-heads, the bracts having brown, scarious appendages. Introduced; in meadows and waste places; rare in England. Flowers July-September.

649 Cichorium intybus *Chicory*

A plant 60-80 cm (2-nearly 3 ft) high, with stiff spreading branches and large, bright blue (rarely white) flower-heads. Locally common on roadsides and in fields, in England and Wales. Flowers July-September.

On the colour plate can be seen a leaf from the lower part of the stem on the left, and the top of a flowering part of the stem on the right.

650 Lapsana communis
Nipplewort

A slender plant, 50-100 cm (20-40 ins.) high, with a much branched stem and small, yellow flower-heads. The lower leaves are lyre-shaped and pinnately divided; the upper leaves are small and entire. The fruits have no pappus. Common in hedges and waste places throughout the British Isles. Flowers July-August.

651 Lactuca muralis
'Wall Lettuce'

A tall plant, 40-100 cm (16-40 ins.) high, with thin, pinnately divided leaves and small yellow, generally only 5-flowered heads in a much branched panicle. Common in woods and hedges in the British Isles.

652 Cicerbita alpina
'Blue Sow-Thistle'

A robust plant, 1-2 m (3-6 ft) high, with pinnately divided leaves and bluish-purple flower-heads in a terminal raceme. Grows in moist places on alpine rocks; very rare.

653 Hypochoeris radicata
'Cat's Ear'

A 30-40 cm (12-16 ins.) high plant with round-toothed leaves in a basal rosette, and erect, leafless stems with large yellow flower-heads, the outer florets grey-green on the outside. There are yellow, scarious scales at the base of the florets. Common throughout the British Isles, in pastures and dunes. Flowers June-August.

654 Hypochoeris maculata
'Spotted Cat's Ear'

A 30-40 cm (12-16 ins.) high plant with leaves in basal rosettes, spotted with brown, stems coarse and stiff-haired bearing large, yellow flower-heads. Rare, in calcareous pastures in eastern and southern counties. Flowers June-July.

655 Leontodon autumnalis
'Autumnal Hawkbit'

A rosette plant, 10-30 cm (4-12 ins.) with pinnatifid radical leaves, branched stems and yellow flower-heads, the ray florets reddish on the outside. Common in meadows and pastures, very common throughout the British Isles. Flowers July-September.

656 Tragopodon pratensis
Goat's Beard, Jack-go-to-bed-at-noon

A tall plant, 30-60 cm (1-2 ft), with stiff, erect branches, narrow pointed leaves and yellow flower-heads, the bracts the same length as the ray-florets. Grows in meadows, pastures and on roadsides; locally common. Flowers June-July.

657 Scorzonera humilis
'Dwarf Scozonera'

A rosette plant, 10-40 cm (4-16 ins.) high, with narrow, basal leaves and generally an unbranched stem, white and woolly when young, bearing a large, pale yellow flower-head. Marshy fields near the sea. Known only in Dorset. Flowers May-June.

658 Sonchus arvensis
'Field Milk Thistle'

A tall plant, 50-120 cm (20 ins.-4 ft), with lobed leaves, coarsely spine-toothed at the edges, and large, golden yellow flower-heads on glandular-haired stalks. Common in salt marshes and on arable land throughout the British Isles. Flowers June-September.

659 Sonchus oleraceus
Sow-Thistle

An erect plant, 25-80 cm (10-32 ins.) high, with soft, lobed, prickly-toothed leaves of a dull green colour, and pale yellow flower-heads. The fruits are transversely 3-ribbed. Common weed on cultivated ground and in waste places throughout the British Isles. Flowers June-September.

659a Sonchus asper
Prickly Sow-Thistle

Resembles the previous species, but differs in having stiff, shiny leaves, less deeply divided, and in the fruits having longitudinal ribs. Common in similar places. Flowers June-September.

660 Taraxacum vulgare
Common Dandelion

A rosette plant with lobed leaves and large yellow flower-heads, singly on thick, hollow stalks, 5-30 cm (2-12 ins.) high. Common in grassy fields, on roadsides, and as a weed in gardens, throughout the British Isles. Flowers May-June.

661 Crepis biennis
Rough Hawk's-beard

A straight, stiff-haired plant, 50-80 cm (20-32 ins.) high, with lobed leaves and fairly large, yellow flower-heads with 2 circles of bracts. Locally frequent in waste places, clover fields and pastures from Central England to Aberdeen. Flowers June-July.

On the colour plate, the top of a flowering plant is shown on the left, a leaf from the lower part of the stem on the right.

662 Crepis praemorsa
'Bitten-off Hawk's Beard'

A 15-40 cm (6-16 ins.) high plant with a rosette of oblong leaves and a leafless, downy stem bearing pale yellow flower-heads in a clusterlike panicle. Grows in meadows and on chalk downs. Flowers in June.

663 Crepis tectorum
'Roof-tile Hawk's-beard'

A slender plant, 25-40 cm (10-16 ins.) high, with greyish down and very narrow stem leaves, the edges rolled back. Flower heads yellow and fairly small. Common in fields and on road-sides. Flowers June-August.

663a Crepis capillaris
'Smooth Hawk's-beard'

Resembles the previous species, but differs in being almost glabrous and in having toothed leaves of a fresh green, the edges not rolled back. Common on grassland and waste places throughout the British Isles. Flowers July-September.

664 Crepis paludosa
'Marsh Hawk's-beard'

A smooth, dark green plant, 30-90 cm (1-3 ft) high, with broad, sharply toothed leaves clasping the stem with their bases, and relatively large, yellow flower-heads. In wet copses and in fens; locally common in the north of the British Isles. Flowers June-July.

665 Hieracium pilosella
Mouse-ear Hawkweed

An 8-20 cm (2-8 ins.) high plant with
runners and flat rosettes of oblong,
stiff-haired radical leaves, downy white
underneath. The pale yellow flower-
heads are carried singly on leafless
stems. Common an dry, sandy pastures
and slopes throughout, the British
Isles. Flowers May-June.

666 Hieracium umbellatum
Hawkweed

A 20-90 cm (8 ins.-3 ft) high plant with a
rosette of small leaves and an umbel-
like inflorescence of yellow flower-
heads, the bracts almost glabrous and
the tips recurved. Common on moors
and dunes throughout the British Isles.
Flowers July-October.

667 Hieracium vulgatum
Common Hawkweed

A 30-60 cm (1-2 ft) high plant with
elliptical, toothed leaves and a wide
corymb of yellow flower-heads with
hairy bracts. Common in woods and on
rocks in Wales, N. England and Scotland. Flowers July-August.

BIBLIOGRAPHY

Flora of the British Isles by A.R. Clapham, T.G. Tutin and E.F. War-
burg. (Cambridge University Press)

Illustrations to the Flora of the British Isles (4 vols.) (Cambridge University Press)

British Flowering Plants by J. Hutchinson (P. R. Gawthorn)

Wild Flowers in Britain by Gaythorne-Hardy (B. T. Batsford)

The Pocket Guide to Wild Flowers by D. McClintock and R.S.R. Fitter.
(Collins)

British Wild Flowers by Patricia Lewis. (The Kew Series)

Oxford Book of Wild Flowers by S. Ary and M. Gregory (Oxford University Press)

Wild Flowers of the Countryside by A. J. Huxley (Blandford Press)

INDEX

The plants listed are in alphabetical order, both the Latin and the common names being included; the numbers given are those of the illustrations and of their descriptions. Where a letter follows a number, the plant is described but not illustrated.